Testimonials from participants

'Looking back at our first course, it's amazing what we've achieved in a short space of time. This isn't a traditional training programme. It's more of a network and a space where women can share their experiences and learn together.'
**Head of Performance and Development, Myra Cooke,
Virgin Atlantic**

'This isn't just about work. It's a whole holistic programme that can be applied to home life as well. It builds assertiveness and confidence and is fully supported by our leadership team.'
Talent Management Consultant, Jen Breach, Virgin Atlantic

'I'm pretty sure without it I would be years behind in my career goals, for fresh out of the "Springboard box"' I applied for the job next on my ideal career progression, my real dream job. I was successful and everything is now heading in the right direction.'
Royal Mail

'Our corporate experience with the Springboard programme shows that it gives women the confidence – and the assertiveness skills – to challenge a traditional "male dominated culture."'
Royal Mail

'This course has been phenomenally good. I'm a far more interested, productive and integrated member of Rolls-Royce for having completed this course.'
Rolls Royce

'The Springboard networking approach in a confidential uplifting environment mean that Rolls-Royce's women employees no longer feel isolated – and they benefit from the experiences of other women, and in particular, the guest speakers.'
Rolls Royce

Springboard®

WOMEN'S DEVELOPMENT PROGRAMME

developed and written by

Liz Willis and Jenny Daisley

revised and updated by

Sue Hewitt

HAWTHORN PRESS

Published by Hawthorn Press, Hawthorn House, 1 Lansdown Lane, Lansdown, Stroud GL5 1BJ, UK
Tel: 01453 757040   Email: info@hawthornpress.com Website: www.hawthornpress.com

Cover design by Francis Porter
Typeset by Frances Fineran
Typeset in Tahoma, Franklin Gothic and Tekton fonts
Printed by Short Run Press Ltd, Exeter

First edition 1990, reprinted 1991
Second edition 1992, reprinted 1993, 1994
Third edition 1995, reprinted 1996
Fourth edition 1998, reprinted 1999
Fifth edition 2000, reprinted 2001, 2002, 2004, 2005, 2006
Sixth edition 2008, reprinted 2008
Seventh edition 2013
Eighth edition 2019

Acknowledgements
Natasha Josefowitz for her kind permission to use her verse Support Systems from her book *Is This Where I Was Going?* published by Columbus Books 1986. Sheldon Press for their kind permission to quote from part of Allan Pease's book *Body Language* 1981. The Training Agency, as it was, for their permission to use Valerie Hammond and Dr Margaret Ryan's material in *Power and Influence in Organisations*. Illustrations by Viv Quillin on pages 42, 104, 174, 177.

ISBN 978-1-912480-09-8

Contents

Foreword

I am delighted to introduce the 8th edition of Springboard. This workbook supports the successful Springboard programme run by women for women.

Gender inequality is often in the news, as women at work are still not on an equal footing with men. Women not reaching their full potential undermines both individual and organisational success. So, despite progress, blockages still remain. Springboard, however, helps women overcome these.

I first came across Springboard in 2001 when, serving as President of the British Association for Women, I cited it as one of the most positive initiatives for women in the police. Then, when I was a senior manager in the Avon & Somerset Constabulary, Springboard enabled talented women in policing to gain the confidence, skills and insights to engage their personal and organisational resources in achieving their goals.

Whilst working for Avon & Somerset, Thames Valley and Cambridgeshire police services, I have seen the benefits of the Springboard Programme. The winning combination of face to face training provides time to reflect and decide where to go, based on your values. Women get fired up, unlocking their potential by seeing what they can achieve. Participants become more confident, resilient and focused. This is good for both for work and home life balance, with participants developing support networks for positive change.

Life is about making the most of it. Springboard invites you to become the best you can be, making your own unique contribution. May you be inspired to make the change that is right for you, and I wish you every success with Springboard and your careers.

Julie Spence
Her Majesty's Lord Lieutenant of Cambridgeshire
Formerly Chief Constable of Cambridgeshire

NOTES

> *Life is the key to everything. Remember, this isn't a dress rehearsal we're going through, it's the real thing.*

Katharine Ross

Begin It Now!

Objectives
- to get you off to a good start
- to start collecting the information you need

This chapter is important because

- how you begin will influence how much you get out of the programme
- channelling your energy enables you to get the best out of yourself
- it represents a golden opportunity

Contents
- our approach
- working with this workbook
- information is power!
- meditation and relaxation
- dealing with change
- your objectives
- the luck challenge
- summary and action
- profile of Donna Thomas

Are you a starter, a runner or a finisher? Beginning well will influence how much you get out of Springboard. Channelling your energy into working through the workbook means you get the best out of yourself. So begin well now!

You are faced with a golden opportunity. Whether you are tackling this workbook on your own or with other people, you have already taken the first step by opening this book and starting. You have either created, or grabbed, the opportunity!

Springboard is all about what you can do for yourself. It's not about what your family, the government, your partner, your colleagues, your manager or your organisation or social network should do for you. You change what you want to change and be who you want to be. You decide which boundaries you want to keep, which you have to keep and which to shift or eliminate completely.

It's about you accepting the responsibility for yourself, realising that no one hands you life on a plate, making the most of everything you've done so far and, looking the world in the eye, believing 'I can do this'.

It is also an unusual opportunity, as most of us don't set aside regular chunks of time to think about ourselves and make positive changes in our lives. You may have decided to do this for yourself, or you may have been encouraged and subsidised by your employer to do so; either way, give yourself a real chance and make the most of it!

More than just a workbook, Springboard is a complete development programme which you can either work through superficially or in as much depth as you want. Also it can be done in lots of different ways such as:
• with workshops in a Springboard Women's Development Programme
• by yourself
• with a few friends
• in support or networking groups

Springboard

- results in practical action
- is about making changes that are appropriate to your life and your circumstances now
- isn't a career directory
- is about you developing yourself as a whole person
- requires you to be self-motivated and committed
- requires energy and enthusiasm
- is relevant to your world today
- puts responsibility for your development clearly with you
- lets you decide what to do with your life
- doesn't contain any magic answers!

Our approach

This book has been developed and written for all women currently in or thinking about being in employment: women who are not at the top of their organisation, i.e. most working women. So this book is for you, whether you're:

- working part-time, full-time or flexibly
- self-employed or working freelance
- looking for work
- considering a return to work
- starting out on your career
- approaching retirement
- not looking for paid work but keen to stretch yourself in other ways
- coping with redundancy
- thinking of setting up your own business
- just promoted
- on a career break or at a crossroads
- in academic life and needing to reassess your goals
- in management and wanting to review and re-plan
- or whatever!

Where do you think you are you at the moment? Are you:

- at a new beginning taking the first steps?
- in a comfortable rut?
- at a crossroads wondering which way to go?
- at the top of a hill, surveying the view and wondering 'What now?'
- discovering that the path you are on is a cul-de-sac?
- finding life quite easy, but unchallenging?
- finding life hard and too challenging?
- going in totally the wrong direction or even backwards?
- soaking your feet in a bucket of water and hoping the pain will go away?
- out of breath and watching others go by?
- on a superb plateau going nowhere?
- having fun, hoping it will last for ever and knowing it won't?
- trudging along and doing OK but welcoming a bit of company on the way?

Wherever you are, you have this workbook because you are a woman wanting to change something.

The content and process of the book are very broad, to encompass women of all ages, at all stages of their lives, of all races, all levels of ability and disability and with all levels of qualifications. The approach is also broad enough to take in the vast array of women's circumstances.

We refer to 'partner' throughout as the close permanent relationship in your life, if you have one. If you're thinking of setting up your own business, of course, you may also have a business partner. We use the word 'work' throughout to mean wherever and however you work. This covers paid, unpaid and voluntary work.

The approach is based on our fundamental beliefs about women's development:

- you can develop yourself more fully, no matter what your circumstances
- you have to want to do it or at least have a sense of questioning where you are now
- you are capable of taking more control over your life
- developing your whole self develops your work life

- women do not always have the opportunities they want to have in a world that is still structured and controlled by men
- small, practical steps work
- the answers lie in the practical experiences of women, both at work and at home
- women develop, achieve and work in a way that is different from men's way
- development can be a difficult process – that's why you have to want to do it
- you can do it – if you want to

We also believe that development, although often challenging and sometimes painful, is enormous fun and leads to greater fulfilment and happiness; so we hope that it will be enjoyable for you, as well as challenging!

 There are four kinds of people in the world:
People who watch things happen,
People to whom things happen,
People who don't know what is happening,
And people who make things happen.

Anon.

Working with this workbook

In this workbook you can do a substantial review of your life, where you are, where you want to be and how to bridge this gap. Work through the chapters in the order they are given, unless you are feeling particularly stressed at the moment, in which case jump to Chapter 9, or, if you are applying for a new job or promotion, leap to Chapter 11! This is your workbook so:

- work through all of it – everything is there for a reason
- keep it safe and private unless you choose to show someone
- work through it as part of the Springboard Women's Development Programme if you are attending one. This means devoting about three hours per week over three months

- treat the workbook as a course and participate in all the bits: inputs, exercises, action points
- decide what you will clear from your diary to make space for you

The workbook flows from looking at yourself and the world about you in the early chapters, through to setting goals and working to achieve them in the later chapters. At the end of the workbook there are useful sources of information and support and also your **Personal Resource Bank** which will help you repeatedly to find the information you need to help you apply for jobs/roles/promotions, reset goals or make changes in your life.

Pages with ☀ are marked so that you can photocopy them before you write on them (pages 84–86) or give them to other people to complete.

Information is power!

You may need more information or you may have too much. With so much and so many types of information available digitally there is a danger of being swamped! Gaining information can increase awareness, minimise risks, give you confidence, energy, ideas and power; looking for information can let people know that you are interested in a topic. If you tend to rush into things without much information, get yourself informed and, if you have too much information, experiment with combining your intuition with fewer facts.

There are a few starter websites on pages 294–305. Keep up to date with forums, look at blogs or YouTube, download podcasts and generally explore what's available. If you are employed make sure that you are familiar with your organisation's intranet and all the resources available internally. Becoming digitally literate is the 21st century equivalent of learning to read and write. Take time to understand and get the most from your digital devices.

Don't forget to also use libraries, books, leaflets, newspapers and magazines. While you are working through Springboard, experiment with reading different material from different sources. Experiment with different social networks, interest groups, downloads and e-learning.

Get your antennae working so that you spot different information and sources of support or advice to help you set and achieve your goals!

People to help you

Later in the workbook you will look in more detail at the people who may help you. Most people will be helpful if you ask them for information or support, particularly if you explain about Springboard. Ask for information, advice, ideas and other contacts. At the end of each chapter there are real stories from other women's development journeys which may give you ideas and inspiration.

Meditation and relaxation

Most chapters also have a short mindfulness meditation or relaxation exercise that you can do to focus your mind during the period of that chapter. If you already follow a particular path of meditation, then use that one. If you don't, simply sit or lie down where you won't be disturbed and allow yourself to relax. Close your eyes or lower them to look at the floor, and breathe deeply by breathing out a little bit extra. If you notice that you can count to two or three as you breathe in then count double that amount, to four or six, as you breathe out. Do that three times and then let your breathing settle. Then start the meditation. It could take you two minutes or ten. That is up to you. These meditations are intended to be positive and helpful so, as a health warning, if you find yourself getting negative or having unpleasant thoughts, then take control and either change the thought or open your eyes and bring yourself out of the meditation.

MEDITATION

The meditation for this chapter is to imagine yourself in a pleasant scene in nature: a beach, a meadow, a wood or wherever. Really notice the environment around you. In the comfortable relaxation of that pleasant place repeat to yourself the word 'release' and as you repeat it let go physically any tension that you can feel in your body. If you become aware of tension and you don't know how to release it, simply give your body a positive instruction such as 'shoulders release', 'neck release'. Don't be tempted to use negative words such as 'stop tensing up' because the subconscious mind still hears 'tensing' and responds by tightening up.

As you let go physically, you can progress to letting go of any other aspects of yourself or your life that you wish to release, such as unhealthy habits or anything that you perceive as holding you back.

When you are ready to stop, become aware of your surroundings and allow yourself to feel the weight of your body on the surface on which it is resting.

Dealing with change

This book is all about making changes. You may love change or hate it, embrace it or shun it!

How do you feel about change? (Write your response in the space below.)

You have probably developed a pattern of coping with change. Some ways of coping are to:
- thrive on it and welcome it
- pretend it's not happening
- insist that the old way is better
- accept it once you've been persuaded
- immediately accept it because it's new
- initiate change yourself

The Kübler-Ross Change Curve

Elisabeth Kübler-Ross developed the approach that follows. Life for most people has ups and downs. Most of us go through stages in response to both personal change, e.g. bereavement, redundancy, relationships, or external change, e.g. software updates, altered bus timetables or new taxes.

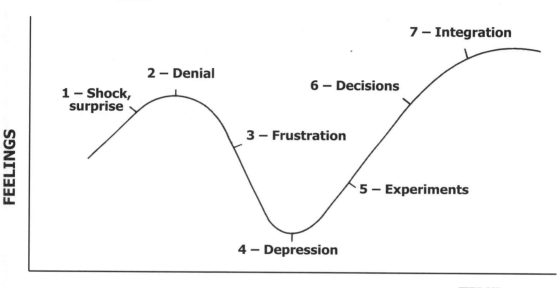

Stage 1

Shock and surprise in response to the event or change. 'I can't believe it!' – whether it's a difficult situation or a lottery win.

Stage 2

Denial of the change and finding ways to prove that it isn't happening. Sticking your head in the sand and reassuring yourself that it isn't really happening. 'I've always done it this way – these new ideas will blow over.'

Stage 3

On the way down, and experiencing anger and frustration. Often a tendency to blame everyone else and lash out at them. Still no acceptance of the change. 'Why pick on me?'

Stage 4

Hitting rock-bottom and experiencing depression and apathy. Everything seems pointless and there is no point in doing anything. 'I'm ready to give up.' Lack of self-confidence.

Stage 5

Stage 4 is so depressing that most of us start to pull ourselves out of it. This is where you will start to try out new things. 'I think I'll have a go at this – after all, anything's better than Stage 4!'

Stage 6

Deciding what works and what doesn't work. Accepting the change and beginning to feel more optimistic and enthusiastic. 'This isn't so bad after all – it actually seems to be working!'

Stage 7

At this stage, you will be integrating the change into your life so it becomes part of your norm – 'The new me!'

YOUR TRACK RECORD WITH CHANGE

Consider where any of your patterns fit with the Kübler-Ross change curve. Think of situations where you have had to deal with change, and assess your track record. These could be at home, at work or any other outside-home involvement, such as voluntary work, clubs or societies.

Changes over which I had no control:

Changes I initiated:

Thinking about the situations, when dealing with change:
* *things I do well are:*

* *things I could improve are:*

Over the next day or two, talk to someone who knows you well and ask them: 'In your opinion, how do I cope with change?' Jot down their reply here:

How does their view compare with how you perceive yourself? Is there a difference between changes at work and changes at home? Perhaps others notice that you cope better than you think you do? What can you learn from the feedback that you've received?

If you are a person who thinks more about the past, it is likely that you will get stuck in feeling depressed (Stage 4) and may tend to slip back to the denial stage (Stage 2). If you are more forward-looking you may be always trying out new ideas (Stage 5) without ever actually moving on to integrate them (Stage 7). Most people have difficulty between the 5th, 6th and 7th Stages.

When Sofia was promoted to Team Leader she went on doing every-thing she always used to do, on top of her new responsibilities (Stage 2). She ended up very overworked and not initially recognising that she needed to allocate more work to her team. She firstly became frustrated (Stage 3) and then quite depressed (Stage 4) before realising that she would need to do things a bit differently (Stage 5). Once she began experimenting, she found the best ways to behave in her new situation. She delegated some of her most familiar tasks, and taught herself how to monitor progress (Stage 6). Once she made her new systems her own, she was fine again (Stage 7).

Your objectives

You may be clear that you want to progress in your life and work, or you may want to get more out of what you're doing now. You may simply want to take three months to review and revise your priorities in life. Whatever your objectives, make sure they're your own, and not what you think your partner, your manager, your parents, your organisation, your Springboard trainer or we would want you to write.

Consider these questions before stating your overall objective. Do you:
- have any specific work or personal goals?
- want to change or get a job?
- want more time to do the things that you want to do?
- know what you want to do?
- have an overall sense of direction?
- know what you don't want to do?
- want to improve your relationships at work and/or at home?
- want to change anything about yourself? If so, what?

What are your objectives in working with this workbook (and the Springboard Women's Development Programme)?

The luck challenge

When we ask women on courses how they've achieved things in their lives, they often say: 'I was lucky' or 'It was just luck really'.

We believe that this is mostly rubbish! When we ask for anecdotal evidence, we then hear wonderful and inspiring stories of women who:

- set themselves goals or took small steps in a direction
- plucked up courage
- picked brains
- kept going despite many difficulties
- made contacts
- volunteered
- told people what they wanted
- had a positive attitude to change
- re-trained

They had developed the right attitude, and taken the right steps to place themselves in the right place at the right time. There was usually an opportunity open to them which they had the courage to grab, and that is the true scale of the 'Luck' that people refer to. When opportunities are there the women who use them are seen as successful. The truly determined don't even wait for opportunities, but stride out positively to make their own.

Most of us say 'it was luck' because it might seem big-headed to say:

'I was the best person for the job.'

'I have good contacts.'

'I was determined to make the grade.'

'I did my background research very thoroughly.'

It feels more comfortable to say 'I was lucky!' The trouble is that after a while you start believing in lucky breaks and waiting for them to happen. You could wait for ever.

We challenge you to take any achievement which you put down to luck, and will guarantee that luck played a very small part indeed. Your luck was your own effort, determination, skills and experience.

We're not saying that there's no such thing as luck; we're simply suggesting that it has a much smaller part to play than most people credit, and that to a large extent you can make your own luck. We subscribe to this well known definition of luck:

 Luck happens when preparation meets opportunity.

This means that you have to do the preparation before you can be ready to seize the opportunity! You will, of course, have done this many times in your life already, but from now on be more aware of the amount of control you have over events.

How is the timing for you?

How are you feeling about all this now?

- impatient to get started?
- wishing you'd never decided to do this?
- anxious or eager?
- ready to make changes?

The timing will never be perfect. A good time is when you feel almost ready for change. You then need a bit of courage to take the plunge. If you wait until you are certain, it may well be too late.

Always be a first-rate version of yourself and not a second-rate version of somebody else.

Judy Garland

Summary and action

In this chapter you've found out about this workbook and its approach. You've got yourself organised and you've made a start.

Action

What actions will you take now? Action points are small, practical, realistic steps with a date for you to complete them by. For example:

- get together with a friend tonight and think of lots of 'me time' ideas
- clear space at home at the weekend to be your work area for this book
- talk to your family on Sunday about support you want for Springboard
- give yourself a treat today – you've started!

Write yours here:

Specific action   **By when?**

Profile *Donna Thomas*

Job Title: Training Sergeant
Organisation: Dyfed-Powys Police

'Square peg in a round hole' is how I have felt as long as I can remember. My father was a soldier. We moved frequently, home life was traumatic and, as a sensitive child, I struggled emotionally. I tumbled into my teens lonely, lost and lacking in confidence. Outwardly a typical teenager, inside I was shy, socially awkward and searching for sanctuary. I learnt to adapt; masking sensitivities, I became independent and resilient.

My parents bought a pub when my father left the army. Increased exposure to people and noise made it difficult to study. As a result my schooling suffered and I failed to achieve the required grades to undertake Psychology at university. Instead I took any course that would accept me, later successfully completing a BSc in Mineral Surveying. To meet financial demands, I worked nights in a factory and joined the Territorial Army. It was tough and being the only woman on my course meant that I again adapted my personality to fit in.

At 23, I returned home, met my husband and had my first daughter. This helped ground me; I felt more secure. I joined the Fire Service to help our finances, delighted to be the first-ever female at my local station. But some of the crew believed their 'tough' profession was not one for a young woman. Training was physically gruelling; I later learnt I was subjected to 'harsher' sessions than normal. Perhaps this was to push me into giving up or prove the demands of the role. Often I was physically sick but I persisted. Unwittingly it served me well; with increased fitness I achieved top student locally and 13th of 8000 applicants for full-time roles. Although I was proud to serve three years, inwardly, I still felt uncomfortable.

I joined the Police Service after my second daughter was born. Determination got me through residential training and I achieved an award for the smartest student; however, I missed my children dreadfully. Over 17 years I have had a successful and varied career despite balancing shift-work with motherhood.

Complex (and often unseen) barriers have made my progression through the ranks challenging. Certainly, poor networking abilities have put me at a disadvantage and, despite some improvements, it is still an unfair playing field for women. I reached a stage where a desire to be authentic became stronger than my ambition to progress and, although I demonstrated high achievement, I withdrew from the process. The choice wasn't easy after the investment of my many years of hard work and study; however, two experiences profoundly changed me and bolstered my decision.

The first was discovering I had the rarest Myers-Briggs personality type. This was extremely empowering, explaining why I felt different to others. I gained self-acceptance which improved my confidence. Interestingly, I discovered my career choices and university course are amongst the worst possible options for my type! Secondly, the sensitivity I had masked for so long manifested as physical symptoms. My fear of being judged, and misplaced need to demonstrate resilience, stopped me seeking help. I became sleep deprived as work pressures significantly increased whilst I was dealing with a difficult bereavement. My body failed; I was diagnosed with chronic fatigue; I had burnt out and spent four months off work.

I now understand that I had unconsciously mimicked my father's traits. My illness was the cost of a lifetime of adapting; doing what I thought was expected, instead of listening to my own needs. Being at rock bottom felt liberating; I set more meaningful goals and finally achieved my teenage desire, taking an MSc exploring Transpersonal Psychology, Consciousness, Quantum Physics and Neuroscience. I regained some equilibrium and returned to work unafraid of being the 'real' me.

I have since become a Blue Light Mental Health Champion and used my research to develop articles, provide speeches, advise leaders and develop a coaching programme to address stress and burnout. This will help front-line workers find new solutions to heal and transform. There must be a lesson here; when I was striving to succeed as the old me, I was going backwards. Now, as my authentic self, I find that a world of opportunity has opened up.

Learning points

- Be yourself. Living in tune with your needs and values will use less of your energy, making success more likely and leading to less stress.
- Undertaking self-development is a great way to gain confidence and self-assurance.
- Overthinking gets you nowhere. Make time for reflection, meditation or creative practice to find more effective solutions. As Einstein said: you cannot solve your problems with the same thinking that created them.
- If you start something that doesn't seem right it's OK to say so and make a different choice.
- Physical, emotional and mental wellbeing are all equally important for a healthy and happy life.

NOTES

> *If women are not perceived to be fully within the structures of power, surely it is power that we need to redefine rather than women?*

Professor Mary Beard
Women and Power: A Manifesto

The World You Live In

Objectives
- to look at the world you live in and identify what impacts on you
- to discover what you know and don't know about the world around you
- to see the bigger picture so that you can decide later what is important for you and your future

This chapter is important because

- you may feel powerful or powerless to influence the world you live in
- the pace of world change is getting faster and you need to know what affects you in your work and personal life

Contents
- your personal power and influence
- your power net
- global issues versus local issues
- facts of the world you live in
- women's lives in the UK
- trends in organisations
- how people get recognition
- indispensable employee tendency
- summary and action
- profile of Ruth Aten-Shearwood

The world that you live in begins with the people you live with and if you live alone it begins at your doorstep. It also arrives in your home through a whole range of digital devices as well as television and radio. From the moment we write this, and you read it, the world you live in will have changed.

You may be very interested and informed about the world that you live in, too busy surviving in it to look any further than the immediate things around you, ignorant about it, naïve, cynical or have a healthy scepticism about it.

Depending on your age, you may be able to see how amazingly the world has changed in your life-time, or how it has changed from your mother's or your grandmother's generation (even if you were not brought up with them). She (or you), perhaps, could not have imagined, a generation or so ago, ordering shopping simply by talking to a digital assistant placed on your kitchen worktop!

Not only is the world changing at a dramatic and accelerating rate but also information about these changes is available instantly across the globe through digital media. When you plan your future or make decisions about your life today, you have much easier access to masses more information than your grandmother did when she was your age. If you can access it and filter it for credibility and relevance, this information about the world and what is happening in it can help you make more informed choices.

For some women, however, there is so much information available with so many conflicting facts and stories that it can seem daunting and the thought of influencing the world can simply feel overwhelming.

In this chapter we will highlight a few current facts to stimulate thought, stir up feelings and motivate you into action, and throughout the rest of the book there will be a few more facts to keep you thinking.

Taking a fresh look at the world about you may give you the clues you need about what you want to do with your life, or may highlight things that you feel energised to do something about. You can decide how to view the reality of the world you live in either from a positive perspective:

The world for women is so much better these days and I can influence making it even better in small and possibly huge ways.

or from a negative perspective:

Isn't it awful all the horrible things that are happening still for women and I can't do anything about it?

or, of course, from anywhere in between.

So, first of all, let's look at your power and influence. We believe that women have much more power and influence than they may realise.

Your personal power and influence

You do not operate in a vacuum. The opportunities that are open to you, the way you are perceived, your ability to influence people, your ability to make things happen, the chances of having your own values met, are all influenced by your confidence in yourself, your judgement and your abilities as well as the culture of your organisation and/or the community you live in. Some women feel that, as individuals, they have very little power, in either their community or the organisation in which they work.

Organisational culture, and the use of influence inside organisations, is often assumed to be about playing office politics, playing games or becoming another rat in the rat race, but it could simply be about understanding what goes on and about being strategic in the way you influence others.

Your personal power is your ability to influence others

At work, at home and in your community, you may have more ability to influence what's going on around you than you think! If you ask someone to do something, and they do it, then clearly you had the ability to influence that person – you were using your personal power in that situation.

Organisational culture and the use of power are entirely neutral. They are the oil that lubricates the cogs of the organisation, and the organisation could, of course, be your family, community or social network.

Your power and influence take several forms.

Formal authority

This is the power invested in you by your job title or your role, e.g. shift leader, mother. Anyone doing your job/role would have your formal authority. It manifests itself in the right to make decisions, and the right to insist that someone does something.

Expertise

This is the power given to you by your specialist or IT knowledge, skills, experience and qualifications. The more exclusive the expertise and the more useful in your social group or workplace, the more power and influence it gives you.

Resource control

Someone may do what you ask them to do because you control their access to something that they want. This power is the control of physical, financial or information resources. For example: car keys, allocation of parking spaces, issuing pocket money, access to people, being budget holder for a project, whether you report back everything that happened at the union meeting, etc. People in relatively low hierarchical positions often have a great deal of resource control power, but the most valued resources are usually money and information.

Interpersonal skills

This is the power you have in the way you get on with people, your ability to persuade and to build good quality relationships, your assertiveness. This is the most potent form of power and can be further developed by anyone.

Your power questionnaire

The following questionnaire is designed to help you think about the power you have, and although it was designed for people in paid employment, the same factors have influence in a voluntary group, family or community:

Formal authority

Do you have the formal right (say, in your job description or role) to make decisions, other than trivial ones?

Do other people need your approval before they take action?

Do you supervise, approve or sign off someone else's work?

Do your decisions significantly affect important aspects of your group or department's work long-term?

Does your manager/partner typically support your decisions and not overrule them?

Do you encounter any resistance to your right to make decisions, supervise others and give approval, from more junior colleagues, peers and more senior people? (If you do, this suggests a reduction in your power which you may need to do something about.)

Expertise

Does it take a year or longer to learn to do your job or role adequately?

Do you need a qualification to do your job/role?

What is the highest qualification in your field? Do you have it?

Are you the only person who can do your job/role?

If you were to leave, would they have difficulty replacing you?

Do your knowledge and skill relate to a major aspect of the group's or department's work?

Do people frequently consult you and follow your advice?

Do more senior people clearly show that they value your contribution?

Resource control

Can you give or withhold access to the following resources?
- money
- information
- ideas
- training
- other people
- login details for software packages or online resources
- perks
- time
- supplies such as pool cars, stationery or other services

Add any others that you control:

Interpersonal skills

Do you make sure that other people take your views seriously when it matters to you?

Are you on good terms with a number of people across different departments and hierarchical levels at work or family, friends and community outside of work?

Do people confide in you?

Are you good at speaking up?

Are you an active listener? Do you make sure you have understood the other person's point of view?

Do you avoid being either passive or aggressive in formal or informal discussion with others at home or work?

Can you hold the attention of a group or larger audience?

Do people have faith in you or goodwill towards you? Do they enjoy making plans with you and support your ideas?

Material used, with permission, from Dr Margaret Ryan's work in *Power and Influence in Organisations,* originally published by The Training Agency.

Your Power Net

Overleaf on page 27 is a diagram of your own power net. Put your own name in the bubble in the centre, as shown in the example on page 26. In the other bubbles put the names of individual people who have an important effect on your life. They may be higher or lower than you in the hierarchy at work, and either inside or outside an organisation. Use the names of individuals and not whole departments, because your power is based on individual relationships. You may want to re-draw the diagram for your life outside of work. Add extra bubbles if you need to. Using the four categories of power outlined on the previous page, assess which sorts of power you are using in your relationship with each person.

ROSALIE'S POWER NET

1 Formal Authority
2 Expertise
3 Resource Control
4 Interpersonal Skills

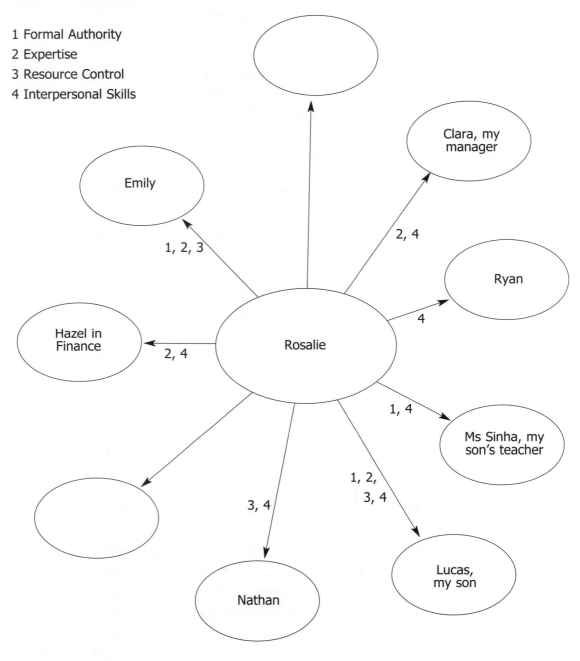

YOUR POWER NET

1 Formal Authority
2 Expertise
3 Resource Control
4 Interpersonal Skills

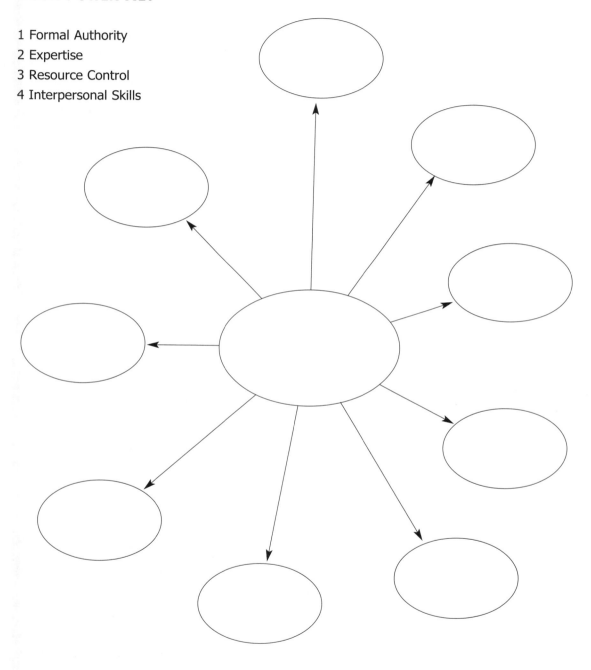

What does it mean?

What have you discovered about how you use your own power? Are you using all your sources of power and influence effectively? Many women underestimate their ability to influence things around them, so you may not have done yourself justice in this exercise. Often women perceive their power as based only on using good interpersonal skills. Also think about what form of power others use to influence you. How are you affected by that?

Make your notes here:

What do you want to change about your power and influence?

The impression of power

Having the formal authority, expertise or resource control is not always enough. Being seen to have it is important. Other people's willingness to be influenced hinges largely on their perception of you, or the impression you create: in other words, your credibility!

At a meeting Ani may have the most expertise on a particular subject, be the most up-to-date and have the most relevant information on it. Also at the meeting is Tina, who knows a great deal less about the subject, but creates the impression that she is a real expert. Tina's ability to influence the meeting may be as great, if not greater, than Ani's, because Tina seems to have more credibility. Sadly, unless Ani does something to change perceptions of her authority, her team may not realise the value of her expertise until after she's left.

So don't assume that people remember your expertise, respect your formal authority, recognise your resource control and value your interpersonal skills. It's up to you to be proud of what you've got going for you and decide how and when to use it positively.

Global issues versus local issues

Where does one begin and the other end? Climate change and the numbers of people still living in poverty throughout the world may seem huge and remote, while joining the local Freecycle group or buying a copy of *The Big Issue* from a homeless person on your local high street may seem more within your sphere. Calculating the impact of transporting food worldwide may seem enormous and daunting, while deciding to buy fresh produce at your local family-run shop may seem more achievable.

Your daily decisions have an impact on the world.

For example: List 10 foods that you buy regularly and then add where they come from.

Food   **Origin**

Deciding to buy a different product or one sourced from a different place is a small act and co-ordinated consumer activism through buying choices has had significant impacts on government and manufacturers.

29

Global issues

Which issues interest you? Do you prefer to hear the good news, e.g.
- a redesigned play area near your childrens' school?
- the saving of thousands of people in a recent disaster?
- research that brings cures closer for chronic disease?
- the joy of a disabled girl's dance group successfully crowdfunding a trip to enter an international competition?

Or do you have concerns about:
- the environment, such as climate change or links between air pollution and asthma?
- activities for young people in your local community that help reduce knife crime or deal with gang culture?
- the plight of women trafficked into the UK?
- the pros and cons of a local wind turbine planning application?
- the health and welfare of refugees escaping conflict zones and living in camps?
- the ethics of keeping wild animals in zoos and safari parks?

Or do you not think about anything like this?

Most people are touched in some way by what is going on around them and can do something about it too.

There is increasing evidence of a new determination amongst women who are not inclined to accept the lives that others decide for them and want to take more control over their own lives and change the world around them. Women are re-shaping the world into something better.

Which issues in your local community or the wider world do you feel strongly about?

What do you want to find out more about?

What are you going to do to become more informed or make a difference?

You cannot take your freedoms for granted. Just like generations who have come before you, you have to do your part to preserve and protect those freedoms, you need to be preparing yourself to add your voice to the conversation.

Michelle Obama

Don't underestimate your influence

Often people feel very strongly about an issue but also feel totally unable to do anything about it. Keep your eyes and ears open for examples of individual people living ordinary lives, changing big things, little by little, by speaking out and by acting locally. The influence of local initiatives such as community gardens, raising funds to keep a women's centre open or social media campaigns can be inspiring examples of the difference each of us can make – you just need to start!

One woman, who had never left the UK before and had no previous legal experience, presented and won her case in the European Court. This resulted in changes in the laws about the use of hazardous chemicals. Her son had died due to the lack of control over the chemicals used in the garage where he worked.

I can promise you that women working together – linked, informed and educated – can bring peace and prosperity to this forsaken planet.

Isabel Allende

Facts of the world you live in

Consider the implications of some of the following statistics. They are intended to inform and provoke thought. Some may be familiar and some may be new to you.

Population

The UK population reached 66 million in 2017, an increase of 4 million since 2009. The year to mid-2016 had the highest population growth, by number of people, since mid-1948. Births account for 41% of the 2017 change. International migration contributes 58%. On average since 2016, 340,000 people leave the UK every year and 610,00 enter. Most of those entering are students or are taking up a firm job offer.

The UK population is 50.7% female and 49.3% male.

There are more people aged 52 than any other age. There are almost equal proportions of those under 18 and over 65 (22.3% and 19.2%, respectively).

Source: ONS Statistical Bulletin: Population Estimates for the UK, England and Wales, Scotland and Northern Ireland: mid-2017, released June 2018

In 2016, there were an estimated 14,910 people aged 100+, 83% of them women. By 2030 there will be 33,200 in this age group.

Sources: ONS dataset 2016: Population Estimates of the Very Old; UN, Department of Economic and Social Affairs, Population Division. World Population Prospects: The 2015 Revision

Employment rates for the over-50s are at their highest since 1984. In 2015, 82% of those aged 25–49 and 69% of those aged 50–64 were employed.

Source: DWP: Economic Labour Market Status of Individuals Aged 50+ since 1984, July 2016

The UK population also includes an estimated:

    13 million disabled people, including 8% of children

    over 8 million people from black and minority ethnic communities

    34 million people who report having no religion

    3.1–4.3 million gay, lesbian or bisexual adults

There are no clear data on the number of trans and non-binary people in the population; estimates vary from 0.2% to 1%.

Sources: DWP Family Resources Survey, March 2018; ONS Census 2011; NatCen Social Attitudes Survey 2017; stonewall.org.uk

Women's lives in the UK

There are 27.2 million UK households, 12.9 million based on marriage or civil partnerships and 3.3 million on cohabiting. There are 2.8 million lone parents and 1.6 million multi-family households. More women than men live alone over the age of 64.

7.9 million families have dependent children; 6.1 million are headed by couples, 2.4 million by a lone mother and 386,000 by a lone father. 40% of people aged 15–34 are living with parents in their family home.
Source: ONS Families and Households, 2016

In 2015, four times fewer single people married, compared with 1973. Women marry younger than men (35 compared with 37 years old). 56% of same sex marriages are between women; the highest number of mixed sex marriages take place when partners are aged 30–35.
Source: ONS Marriages in England and Wales, 2015

Women at work

Over the last 30 years there has been a significant increase in women's participation in the labour market. In 2017 there were 15.1 million women in employment and the female employment rate was 70% compared with 79% for men. 42% of women work part-time compared with 13% of men.

The gender pay gap for all employees is 17.9% in favour of men. For full-time roles men earn 9.1% more than women. The gap widens after the age of 30, coinciding with more women working part-time and men moving into management roles. Men earn more in all full-time occupations, ranging from a 4.9% pay gap in sales and customer service to 23.9% for skilled trades roles.

5% of women of working age are involved in business start-ups (12% of men) and 20% of small businesses are led by women. In 2018, 28.7% of directors of FTSE 100 companies were women, up from around 15% in 2011. Women made up 23.4% of FTSE 250 directors; there are eight all male boards in the FTSE 250, but none in the FTSE 100.
Sources: House of Commons Briefing Paper: Women and the Economy, March 2018
ONS Release: Gender Pay Gap in the UK, October 2018

In his 2015 report Lord Davies praised businesses for achieving the target of 25% women on boards which he set in 2011. He set a new target of 33% women's representation on FTSE 350 boards by 2020.

Source: BIS Davies Report, Women on Boards: 5 Year Summary Report, October 2015

36% of headteachers/principals in state secondary schools and academies are women, compared with 74% of all teachers.

19% of university vice chancellors and 25% of professors are women.

43% of senior civil servants and 54% across the service are women.

24% of senior police officers are women compared with 29% of all ranks.

20% of the senior judiciary and 46% of tribunal judges are women.

Women are 3.6% of senior and 10% of regular roles in the armed forces.

15% of sport's governing body chairs are women.

28% of charities' CEOs are women.

Of non-royal historical statues commemorating achievement 5% are of women.

16% of directors of British films and 32% of cast members are women.

Sources: Fawcett Society: Sex and Power, April 2018, HESA HE Staff Statistics, January 2018; Home Office: Police Workforce Dataset, March 2017; Institute for Government Explainer: Gender Balance in the Civil Service, August 2018; Sky News: Military must do more, https://tinyurl.com/yddrpbzx, June 2018; Lord Chief Justice: Judicial Diversity Statistics, July 2018

Women in public life

Women's representation in the UK Parliament has increased from 4.3% in 1974 to 32% in 2017. This contrasts with the Scottish Parliament (35% women) and the National Assembly for Wales (43% women), where more equal representation has been achieved through positive action. The Northern Ireland Assembly is 30% female. In total 490 women have been elected to parliament since 1918. The four longest-serving women MPs have between them 133 years in Parliament.

There are 52 black and minority ethnic MPs, 15 Muslim MPs and one Sikh. There are five MPs with a disability and 45 openly LGBT MPs.

Women make up 28% of local councillors in England and 27% of local councillors in Wales. The London Assembly is 40% female. Women make up just 17% of council leaders.

Sources: Fawcett Society: Sex and Power, April 2018; House of Commons Library: Social Background of MPs 1979–2017 and Women Members of Parliament: Background Paper.

UK is ranked 48th globally for representation of women in parliament.

Source: www.parliament.uk/briefing-papers

Women at home

The global 'housework gap' has narrowed since the 1960s, when women did at least 85% of unpaid household work. On average women now spend 132 minutes on housework daily (including 62 minutes cooking) compared with men's 69 minutes (31 mins cooking). Men average less than 2 hours of childcare per week compared with women's 4.7 hours. The only area where men do more unpaid work hours is in the provision of transport, including driving themselves and others around, as well as commuting to work.

Sources: Centre for Time Use Research www.timeuse.org; ONS: Women shoulder the responsibility of unpaid work, November 2016.

Men in the UK are three times more likely to have saved enough money for retirement than women. 15% of men have more than £300,000 in pension savings, the typical amount someone on average wages would need to keep their current lifestyle in retirement. Just 4% of women have this much in pension savings and 15% of women have no savings at all.

The gender pension income gap is £85 per week, with men predicted to receive £401 to women's £316.

Source: The Actuary: 10th August 2018 and 26th March 2018.

Women at risk

Care note: This section includes facts about crimes against women and children. Sources of support can be found in Chapter 14.

25% of women will experience domestic abuse in their lifetime. Two women are killed each week in the UK by their partner or ex-partner. In the year to March 2016 1.2 million women reported experiences of domestic violence in England and Wales. Women experience an average of 35 incidents of domestic violence before going to the police. It is estimated that around three women a week commit suicide due to domestic violence.

Source: www.refuge.org.uk

20% of women aged 15–64 have experienced some form of sexual violence. Nearly half a million adults are sexually assaulted each year in England and Wales. Only 15% of those who experience sexual violence choose to report it to the police.

Three-quarters of all adult service users contacted Rape Crisis Centres about sexual violence that took place at least 12 months earlier; 42% were adult survivors of child sexual abuse.

6% of reported rapes end in a conviction.

Source: www.rapecrisis.org.uk

In 2017, the Forced Marriage Unit (FMU) gave advice or support related to a possible forced marriage in 1196 cases. 77% of cases involved women and 58% of cases concerned people under the age of 25.

In the same year the FMU handled cases related to 65 countries, those with the highest number of cases being Pakistan, Bangladesh, Somalia and India. Although overseas travel can be involved, 11% of cases related to potential or actual forced marriage happened entirely in the UK.

In 2015/16 there were 53 prosecutions for forced marriage and 32 convictions.

Sources: www.gov.uk/guidance/forced-marriage; www.cps.gov.uk

Female genital mutilation has been illegal in the UK since 2003. It is estimated that 23,000 girls are cut in the UK every year and that in 2011 137,000 women and girls with FGM were living permanently in the UK.

Nearly 200 FGM protection orders have been issued since 2015, to protect girls at risk of FGM. Since 2010, 36 cases of FGM have been referred to the Crown Prosecution Service. The first conviction for FGM was in early 2019. Three earlier cases resulted in acquittals.

Sources: dofeve.org; Metropolitan Police; City University: Prevalence of Female Genital Mutilation in England and Wales, July 2015; *The Guardian,* March 2018

https://tinyurl.com/yaxuw9p9

Trends in organisations

Meetings now frequently take place via Skype, Zoom or other digital conference software and face-to-face training is supplemented with webinars and online modules including MOOCs.

The concept of a career or job for life is now obsolete. Many people have portfolio careers, combining a mixture of roles or job types.

Central government funding to public sector organisations is severely reduced so they have had to become more entrepreneurial and income-generating and work more in local partnerships.

Organisations are reducing the numbers of full-time employees and contracting out work to freelance people and/or increasing the number of part-time employees including those on zero hours contracts.

The 'gig economy' has expanded, supported by digital platforms. The number of people in freelance or short-term roles such as an Uber driver, delivery biker or Taskrabbit has increased significantly.

Climate change has become a live issue for everyone with public pressure, forcing organisations to make green commitments such as reducing or ending plastic usage.

There are expectations (and legal requirements) for employers to provide flexible working patterns such as job-sharing, shared parental leave, term-time only working, flexitime and other family-friendly policies.

The 'always on' smart phone means that employees often feel under pressure to respond to work emails out of hours.

Women and older workers represent under-developed sources of labour for employers. Organisations with over 250 employees must publish their gender pay gap.

Data security has become a personal, public sector and commercial issue with large-scale data-breaches on the increase.

Many people don't have their own workspace but hot-desk or work in co-working areas. Increasingly there is no desktop computer, but a portable laptop or tablet.

More people are able to work from home, access work data online or over a secure network. Increasingly, a wide range of employees want to have the flexibility to work anywhere without having to be in a specific building to do so.

Organisations increasingly communicate with customers via apps and social media.

Consider what these trends might mean to you. Opportunity or threat?

What is your attitude to the fast changing digital environment?

How will you discover what you may need to know for your future work?

Look for any recent initiatives in your organisation, such as:

- webinars and online training
- coaching and mentoring schemes
- support for gaining professional qualifications
- women-only courses
- career breaks and flexi-working
- corporate social responsibility projects
- work from home opportunities

Add any others:

Take a look at your own organisation

In a huge and diverse organisation some of the general culture may affect you greatly, or have only a small effect. In a small organisation it may affect every aspect of your work. It's likely that the day-to-day culture of your own workplace has a dramatic effect on your morale, and your opportunities for change.

THINK THROUGH THESE ASPECTS

What is the structure of your organisation? Is it flat or hierarchical?

Are there particular areas where people get promoted quickly? If so, which?

What is highly valued, e.g. loyalty, bright ideas, independence of thought, long service, attention to detail, achieving targets?

Which people hold the influence, e.g. those with new ideas, those who walk the talk?

Is there an inner circle of people who hold the influence? If so, why? How can an outsider get to know them?

What are the anecdotes that are told fondly about the organisation or about past members of the organisation?

Where is the organisation going? Is there a sense of direction?

What do you know about the people who use your organisation's goods/services?

Who decides what happens in your workplace?

Overall, how is the culture of your own place of work affecting you and your ability to achieve your ambitions?

WHAT DOES IT ALL MEAN TO YOU?

Considering all these facts and trends:

What surprises you or confirms what you already know?

What opportunities are offered to you by these facts and trends?

What threats are posed to you by these facts and trends?

How will they influence the important people in your work life?

How will they influence the important people in your personal life?

How people get recognition

If you're waiting to get promoted, move sideways or change your job in any way, it is important to consider how you are perceived. Harvey Coleman (ex-IBM) identified three factors contributing to people gaining access to opportunities such as interesting projects or promotion.

Performance

the reality of how good your work actually is.

Image

the impression you create about yourself and your work. Some people are overlooked for opportunities because while their work is actually good they create the impression of being unfocused, insecure, lacking in motivation or ambition, negative and not interested in opportunities.

Visibility

whether people know about you and your work. This means raising your profile, becoming more visible and building your contacts. You may do a great job, create the right impression, but if the right people don't know that you exist you won't get access to opportunities or recognition for what you do.

The contribution of each of these factors was:

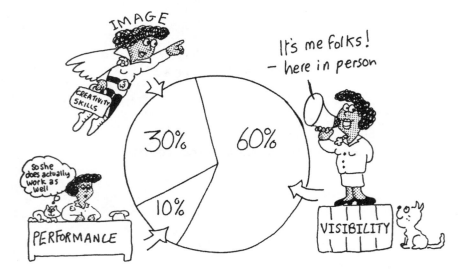

It may seem outrageous that the quality of your work contributes only 10% towards getting recognition or access to opportunities. Performance is still important, but on its own won't get the juicy opportunities coming your way.

There are usually several people who are capable of doing a job – the person who gets it also has the impression she creates and her visibility working for her. These statistics are not saying 'Don't bother to turn in a good performance' but they are saying:

'Perform well, and don't wait to be recognised or rewarded.'

'Perform well, and put some effort into building your reputation as well.'

These statistics go a long way towards helping with 'IET'.

Indispensable Employee Tendency

Indispensable Employee Tendency (IET) is a phenomenon that affects women much more than men. You will find it in every organisation, and often in every family or community.

The Indispensable Employee is the person who thinks that development, advancement or recognition come with doing a good job and being helpful. She believes that if she works well enough, hard enough and helps everyone around her, someone will notice and reward her. If advancement or recognition doesn't happen, she may interpret that as implying she's not doing enough, so she works harder, better and maybe longer hours.

She is holding the place together; they couldn't cope without her. It sounds like a good career plan.

But she may never be able to move on, because the whole place or project would fall apart – it's much better to take the risk with someone who's not indispensable.

She is often asked to train up new people who then get promoted over her head. At home she believes that people do appreciate her – it's just that they're too busy to show it.

She doesn't know that 90% of the reason she is not progressing is she's lost herself in the work, she doesn't realise how she's perceived, that in becoming indispensable she's not making efforts to create the right impression of where she aims to be.

IET can lead to bitterness, frustration and exhaustion with being stuck in a role you can't seem to escape from. Instead aim to be valued not indispensable.

Image

Demonstrate what you are capable of and your interest in being stretched. Let your achievements shine – don't keep them a secret.

Visibility

Build a strategic network of contacts and talk to them about your successes and share your aspirations. Raise your profile by asking to shadow senior colleagues; attend meetings and put your ideas forward; take part in staff suggestions schemes; write something for the newsletter or blog. Remember also to use social media for extending your contacts.

YOUR IET TRAITS

What traits do you display that could indicate IET? Do you show these at work, at home or in other life areas?

What do you want to do about it?

Summary and action

In this chapter you've looked at just some of the things that are going on around you and begun to assess where the opportunities lie for a change.

Further optional reading

Chimamanda Ngozi Adichie – *We Should All Be Feminists* (Fourth Estate)
Laura Bates – *Everyday Sexism* (Simon and Schuster)
Mary Beard – *Women and Power: A Manifesto* (Profile Books)
Joanna Williams – *Women vs Feminism* (Emerald)
Inge Woudstra – *Be Gender Smart* (Panoma Press)
Richard Templar – *The Rules of Work* (Pearson)

Action

What action are you going to take to make the most of the opportunities open to you?

Here are some suggestions:
- tomorrow search for relevant webinars
- next week find out about the gender pay gap in my organisation
- find out more about self-employment over the next month
- ask my boss tomorrow when I can represent them at meetings
- make time next month for the women's network
- talk to my partner tonight about the statistics in this chapter
- visit the community centre next week to find out about local projects I could be involved in.

Write yours here:

Specific action   **By when?**

Profile *Ruth Aten-Shearwood*

Job Title: Service Manager, Brokerage (Adult Care)
Organisation: Derbyshire County Council

I think that my life story has been about change and
challenge. I've been fortunate in many ways. I was
adopted at birth and grew up in Dallas, Texas with an
adoptive family who valued education and allowed me to pursue my
goals. I had a 'normal' upbringing, but I knew I was different, not just from my
family. I never felt I fitted in; deep down, part of my identity was missing. In
searching for it I tried many things: sports, playing the violin, reading. I wasn't
always successful but kept trying. Perseverance I have always had.

When I was a teenager my parents split up. I was coming to terms with my
own sexuality – I found I wasn't attracted to boys, and family relationships
were strained. There were arguments and tears and finally, in my adult years,
a degree of acceptance. Probably to make up for perceived rejection, I became
determined to achieve. I joined the US Marine Corps at 20 and later worked as
a Secretary in the Environmental Protection Agency, also attending university
at night to complete a degree. It worked well for me. My understanding boss
allowed me to study when I didn't have pending work to do. After my degree I
served as a Police Officer/Criminal Investigator in Colorado for 17 years. I think
these years, although rewarding, were certainly about challenge and testing
my limits.

Ten years ago, on my birthday, I saw, on an obscure 'dating' part of Facebook,
an interesting profile of a British woman with whom I seemed to have lots in
common. We started emailing but I certainly had no any intention of dating
someone 5,000 miles away. There is a list of 'important life changes' that
experts say you shouldn't do all at once. Things like 'moving house', 'starting a
university course' and 'starting a new relationship'. Within nine months I had
completed most of these! I'd sold all but the house in Colorado, quit my job
and moved to England. My family thought I had lost my mind. I became a
step-parent to two teenagers, started a Master's degree and took a new job in
social work.

My partner and I were joined in a civil partnership and five years later converted it to marriage.

The tipping point for me was that I had achieved everything I thought I would. I had all I needed materially and lacked a meaningful personal relationship. It felt the right time to embark on the adventure of living in a new country. It was also much easier for me to go East than uproot my future partner and her two teenagers, disrupting their good relationship with their Dad. I was also influenced by legal changes in the UK giving marital rights to same sex couples. It took another six years for this to happen in the USA. I love living in the UK, love my wife and family and have never looked back. We visit my US family, but my life and purpose, heart and head, belong here in the UK.

Within a few years of starting my social work job with a local authority I applied for a management role. I was really surprised to get the interview, much less the post. Since then, I have steadily progressed professionally. I think a lot of this is because I accept change, focus on solutions and face challenge head-on. It isn't always easy. I've learned that it's OK to fail as long as you get up, brush yourself off and try again. You may have to change your approach, but never give up.

A final little update: This year, for the first time ever, I've been able to jointly celebrate my birthday with my biological Mum. We heard each other's voices for the first time only last year. A DNA test revealed my birth family to me, and, following additional research, I finally made contact by sending a Christmas card.

In spring this year my wife and I travelled to South Carolina and met lots of new friends and relatives. So, I have two families now, the one that raised me and the one that created me. Both have been so loving and supportive through this whole discovery. I feel fortunate, as it doesn't always work out like this for adopted children. I've also been lucky that my adoptive family do not seem to be threatened by the discovery, which was my greatest fear in all of this. The next chapter in my life has started and I'm excited to see where it leads.

Learning points

- Don't be frightened of change. It is a constant in our lives and can present many new opportunities. The best solution is to face it head-on.
- If you feel there are gaps in your life or identity keep searching until they are filled. You will know when it's right.
- Failing is just part of the cycle of growth. If we never failed we would never achieve. Have a strategy to deal with setbacks and recognise that they will happen.
- Strive to be you, not the version of you that everyone thinks you should be.

NOTES

3

> *When I am trusting and being myself as fully as possible, everything in my life reflects this by falling into place easily, often miraculously.*

Shakti Gawain

Who Are You?

Objectives
- to assess who you are now
- to make the most of the best of you

This chapter is important because

- understanding who you are and what you believe in helps you take the next step
- learning from your experiences moves you onwards
- identifying your values clarifies your goals
- letting go of old patterns helps you think more freely about the future

Contents
- your whole self
- overcoming prejudice
- becoming an experiencing person
- your values
- your attitude
- summary and action
- profile of Sheree Axon

Knowing yourself

Whoever you are and wherever you are in your life you have this workbook because you are a woman wanting to change something or do things better or differently in the future.

The UK has legislation making it illegal to discriminate against a person on account of gender or gender reassignment, race, colour, disability, age, sexual orientation, or religion. Organisations declare themselves as 'Equal Opportunities' or 'Diversity' employers. The past climate, however, has resulted in the majority of senior posts being held by **men** and **White, heterosexual, non-disabled, cis-gendered (non-trans) people**.

Your whole self

If you are White, heterosexual and non-disabled, it may be that you have not thought much about some of the issues that follow. On the other hand you may have thought a great deal about them because they are very relevant to you or to someone close to you. Work through all the parts of the chapter so that you take in issues for other women as well as for yourself.

In our society there is considerable prejudice and discrimination against groups who are under-represented, misrepresented or stereotyped. Prejudice is the prejudgement of a person, not based on reason or knowledge. Prejudice affects the behaviour of both the minority and the majority. Prejudice usually arises out of fear and lack of knowledge. Acting on our prejudices can lead to discrimination. Often women have experienced discrimination but pass it off as 'humour'. Everyday discrimination can become so commonplace it seems normal and acceptable, with many people not noticing it happening around them or to them.

Being a woman

Being a woman is at the core of who you are. Usually the first thing that people notice about each other is the gender that they are. Some women, assigned male at birth, have affirmed their gender as a woman, often after a long and challenging process. So if you have had your gender re-assigned you will have thought a lot about what it means to you to be a woman. Otherwise being a woman is all you have known and you may or may not have thought about it very much. Your relationship to your gender may also be hugely affected by surgery (mastectomy, hysterectomy), inability/difficulty in conceiving or by the menopause.

Being your age now

At the age that you are now you are likely to have experiences in common with other people around the same age. Although some of these may reflect patterns general to women and men from earlier generations, their experiences will have been substantially different. At your age in the 21st century, the speed of global communication, access to information, morality and standards of behaviour and many more aspects of life are very different from how they were in your mother's or grandmother's time. Similarly your experience of life 10 or 20 years ago is very different from how people 10 or 20 years younger than you experience their life now.

Being your race or ethnic origin

Similarly, being the race that you are may open or close doors for you. Black and minority ethnic women face structural barriers such as services, public policies and recruitment methods that are exclusive. Social stereotypes and racism also affect attitudes and behaviour experienced, from violent race hate crimes to media bias and exotification, from stereotyping excused as 'banter' to receiving judgemental looks.

In 2016 the employment rate for Pakistani/Bangladeshi women was 35% compared with 71% for White British women. Indian women had the highest employment rate of all black and minority ethnic groups at 64%.

Men and women from the Indian ethnic group reported an average score for happiness higher than the national average, and people from the Black and Mixed ethnic groups reported average scores lower than the national average.

Source: DWP: Ethnicity Facts and Figures, Employment & Health, January 2018.

Being disabled or non-disabled

Society is largely set up to work well for non-disabled people, with many buildings, services, job criteria, websites and opportunities designed without input from, or consideration of the needs of and barriers for, disabled people. Examples of barriers include meeting rooms with no induction hearing loop for Deaf people, courses with learning materials that don't work well with Dyslexia, and websites that are incompatible with screen readers used by Blind and partially sighted people.

As well as physical barriers, attitudes and behaviours can also be disabling, for example social stigma around mental health difficulties, lack of understanding of invisible illnesses and reactions to facial disfigurement. Disabled women are under-represented in many areas of employment, political appointments and the media; many disabled women face additional disadvantages around body image, independence and safety compared with non-disabled women.

Having your spiritual or religious beliefs

The UK is a multi-belief country and many people follow specific, clear and defined spiritual or religious paths. Your beliefs may be a big part of your identity and how others perceive you or an invisible aspect of your private thoughts. Many people are humanists or non-religious or may also hold beliefs, for example, about natural healing, veganism, peace, feminism, socialism.

Having your sexual orientation

This means being heterosexual, lesbian, bisexual or pansexual. You may have experienced feeling oriented towards people romantically, sexually or intellectually. There is increasing recognition of romantic diversity and the role of celibacy and asexuality. Your sexual orientation may not play a huge part in your life, and your arrival at your current sense of who you are sexually may be something that you have given little thought to. Or it may have been a long and challenging process for you to be who you are now with your sexual orientation.

While my mixed heritage may have created a grey area surrounding my self-identification, keeping me with a foot on both sides of the fence, I have come to embrace that. To say who I am, to share where I am from, to voice my pride in being a strong, confident mixed-race woman.

Meghan Markle

Overcoming prejudice

Your gender, sexual orientation, age, race, colour and level of disability may all have an impact on the people you meet. The degree of impact varies according to the degree of prejudice you hold and meet. When prejudice continues over a period of time, people change their behaviour to overcome it, fight it or give in to it. You may experience prejudice from others or you may be prejudiced about others.

To overcome your or other people's prejudice, what parts of your behaviour do you want to change if you encounter prejudice on account of:	People being prejudiced about me	My prejudice about other people
Being a woman?		
Your age?		
Your race or colour?		
Being disabled or having experience of health or learning difficulties?		
Your spirituality/religion/belief?		
Your sexual orientation?		
Anything different or unusual about you? e.g. class, being very tall/short, having an accent		

53

'
A lot of different flowers make up a bouquet.
Muslim origin
,

Becoming an experiencing person

Becoming a fully experiencing person means:
- learning from your experience
- being open to what life brings you
- having a positive attitude to life
- regarding failure as an opportunity to learn and grow
- actively changing and growing
- learning something new from every year of your life, rather than experiencing the same year over and over again
- meeting every new situation afresh without old preconceptions or rules affecting you
- being an independent thinker; thinking things out for yourself instead of accepting other people's views
- having a healthy curiosity about your past and what you can learn from it to help you in the future

The following exercise exploits your healthy curiosity and extends your process of learning from everything that has happened to you.

THIS IS YOUR LIFE

List the events that have happened in your life so far. Events can be:
- something you remember for no specific reason
- happy or sad
- fearful, funny or embarrassing
- success or failure
- challenging
- new or repetitious
- very short experiences, anything from a chance remark that sticks in your head, to a long summer holiday
- life changing or insignificant

People usually remember more if they start now and go backwards, so start with your age now and work backwards, just putting a key word or two for each event until you reach your earliest memory. Do it briskly without going into too much detail. If you want more room transfer this onto a bigger sheet of paper.

MY LIFE

Now create a pictorial representation, an image or images, on this page to show how your life has been. Be as creative as you like with how you show it.

You can draw pictures or icons, create a graph of the ups and downs, construct a flow chart, take a larger sheet and cut out pictures from magazines to represent the events. Use colour and shapes if you wish.

Step out of the history that is holding you back.
Step into the new story you are willing to create.

Oprah Winfrey

TRACKING DOWN THE THEMES

Look at your images on the previous page as if it were someone else's and pick out the themes. Timing is a theme and a good place to start.

What major events have you experienced earlier or later than most people? e.g.

- death of a close friend or relative
- taking responsibility or caring for others
- notable achievements
- gaining qualifications
- experiencing serious illness
- marriage/civil partnership/divorce
- puberty/menopause/childbirth

Search for other themes. What strikes you most as you look at your images?

What themes or threads run through your life?

What are the key turning points?

What do you notice that you would like to let go of? e.g. themes, relationships that are not helping you, ties that are binding you to the past, humiliations, resentments

How do you rate yourself in terms of success/failure?

What have you learnt from this exercise?

Your values

Your approach to life is based on a set of beliefs that you have acquired over the course of your life so far. Some of these will be truly yours and some may have been acquired from the environment you have lived in. All your decisions are based on what you value. Values are your beliefs, and give you the criteria by which you measure things.

Very often, when people say 'I can't ...' what they really mean is 'I don't choose to ...'

You are making lots of choices about your life all day, every day in the way that you:
- choose to behave
- respond or react to situations
- prioritise your time/place in relationships and activities
- use your money/time/energy
- relate to the rest of the world/your community
- think and feel about yourself

If you are indecisive, then even choosing not to choose also affects the way you spend your life, so there's no avoiding your own influence! The way you make these day-to-day split-second choices is strongly influenced by what matters to you and what you believe in – that is, your values. Knowing your values tells you what you want to do, don't want to do, are likely to enjoy doing or feel strongly about.

‘

My story is a freedom song of struggle. It is about finding one's purpose, how to overcome fear and stand up for causes bigger than one's self.

’

Coretta Scott King

Values change over time, i.e. as you get older, and/or as circumstances change. For example, starting work, having children, being left alone. Finding new information often triggers the connection to our values. If you read an article, see a film or TV programme, find something on your social media newsfeed or hear something from a friend, it is seldom that you are neutral to the information. Usually you have a response or reaction to the information. Most people have a pattern of response. Is it good news that really captures your imagination or is it the negative news that fires your feelings? Your responses could be:

Neutral – no strong feelings or apathetic, don't care, not affected
Positive – happy, pleased, energised, ecstatic, interested, moved to tears, joyful
Angry – irritated, annoyed, furious, outraged
Sad – upset, depressed, tearful
Fearful – anxious, frightened, scared, apprehensive, petrified
Guilty – ashamed, responsible, 'I should do something'

The type and strength of your response usually indicate that the news you have received matches or crosses one of your values.

Think back to the facts given in Chapter 2 and read the following information to see what arouses feelings in you that may be related to your values. Some of this information shows an improvement on the situation for women 30 years ago.

There are 700 million illiterate adults in the world and two-thirds of them are women. In 43 countries, young women aged 15–24 are still less likely than young men to have basic reading and writing skills.

130 million girls between the age of six and 17 are out of school and 15 million girls of primary-school age, half of them in sub-Saharan Africa, will never enter a classroom.
Source: Unesco World Literacy Day' September 2017 (www.uis.unesco.org)

About 830 women die around the world every day from pregnancy or childbirth-related complication. Almost all of these deaths occur in developing countries, and most could be prevented.
Source: World Health Organisation: Maternal mortality, February 2018 (www.who.org)

630 million live in extreme poverty, 8% of the world's population. Poverty is rising in some parts of Africa and South America. The current escape rate from poverty is 1.1 people per second, against the goal of 1.6.
Source: The World Poverty Clock; running live until 2030 (worldpoverty.io)

In the UK more than one in five people (22%) are living in poverty, defined as having family income of less than 60% of the median income for their family type, after housing costs. This includes 8.1 million working-age adults, 4.1 million children and 1.6 million pensioners. Over 7% of people have lived in poverty for three out of the last four years (persistent poverty) and a quarter of these are lone parent families. Action to reduce housing costs for renters, strengthen social security support and open up better paid work opportunities could significantly reduce these figures.
Source: UK Poverty 2018, Joseph Rowntree Foundation, December 2018

815 million people do not have enough to eat, 60% of the world's hungry are women. Hunger kills more than AIDS, malaria and TB combined.
Source: The Hunger Project: World Hunger Day 2017

In 2018, none of the 193 UN Member nations is on track to achieve the 17 UN Sustainable Development Goals by 2030. Some of the biggest achievement gaps relate to universal provision of secondary education. Although richer nations are eliminating poverty they are not moving fast enough on climate action, sustainable production and protecting biodiversity.

Source: www.sdgindex.com

Values

Values relate to the four different areas of your life – the world/community, work, relationships and yourself. All these areas overlap, may be in conflict and may have common denominators. For example – valuing working for the community versus wanting or needing to make a lot of money may create a dilemma.

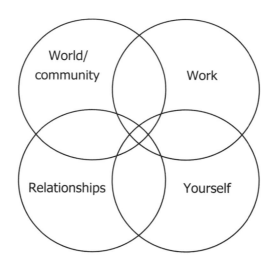

World/community	The global village: your local area and people, your town or hockey team, your continent or church, global oceans, space, mountains, the park.
Work	What you do to pay the bills or contribute: salaried, volunteering, internship or studying.
Relationships	Connections with those around you and closest to you: family, partner, neighbours, colleagues, friends.
Yourself	Your living, breathing, human self.

WHAT DO YOU VALUE?

What matters to YOU? What is important? What do you value?

Write down the things you value on the chart on the next page. Use the examples to give you ideas – or cover them up if you wish to be left free to find your own ideas first.

At work
a job
fair salary
challenge and interest
environmental impact
responsibility
travel
working with people
making a difference
producing a product/service I value

For the world/community
a safer crossing near the school
litter being cleared from the High Street
peace
no child abuse
everyone with food and water
free political systems
stop climate change
end modern slavery
equality

In your relationships
honesty
someone special
children of my own
shared values
sense of humour
security
to be valued as me
space for myself

For yourself
sense of humour
peace of mind
creative activities
time to dig the garden
good health
a nice car
house decorated to my taste
having self-respect
time to read a book

Value	I MUST have	I would like to have
Work		
World/ community		
Relationships		
Myself		

Meeting values raises energy

When your values aren't being met, it gives rise to dissatisfaction, complaints and niggles, and your energy drains away.

When your values are being met, it brings satisfaction and good feeling, and your energy rises. Values are so personal that no two people have the same lists. There are no right values or wrong values, only your values.

On the chart tick your values that are being met at the moment.

Sharing values

Some people find it easier to share personal things such as values with people they are really close to. Others prefer to share with people they don't know so well.

Sharing has the advantages that you:
• become clearer about your own ideas
• pick up hints and tips from others
• think about and assess what you've written

There is no need to get very heavy about it – even though values are a serious personal issue. Get together with or telephone two or three other women and share your ideas. Then add any new ideas to your list.

Are you fulfilled?

If you have values in the 'I must have' section which aren't being met, then these may give you the clues about the goals that you want to set for the future.

In the 'I must have' column for the world it may seem daunting to think of tackling world hunger or pollution. Acknowledge the values now and wait till later to think about how you will meet them.

If people have large numbers of unfulfilled values in the 'I must have' section, they may respond by:
- gaining the drive and determination to do something about it
- becoming bitter and cynical
- daydreaming wistfully about what might have been
- complaining that life isn't fair

How do you feel about your fulfilled values?

How do you feel about your unfulfilled values?

Which unfulfilled values do you want to do something about?

If you were to distil your values down to seven words that you could use to check out your future decisions, what would these words be?

Then you can ask yourself a question, such as:
'For me, would this decision make life … (insert your seven words)?'

On the following pages you'll find a list of values words which can help you consider which matter to you most.

Values words

Abundance	Daring	Freedom
Acceptance	Devotion	Friendship
Achievement	Dignity	Fun
Adventure	Discovery	Generosity
Amusement	Diversity	Gentleness
Appreciation	Education	Grace
Artistry	Effectiveness	Gratitude
Arousal	Efficiency	Greatness
Authenticity	Emotion	Growth
Beauty	Empathy	Guidance
Bliss	Empowerment	Harmony
Caring	Enabling	Health
Charity	Endeavour	Honesty
Choice	Energy	Honour
Commitment	Enlightenment	Humour
Community	Environmental awareness	Imagination
Communication	Equity	Improvement
Compassion	Ethics	Inclusion
Competency	Excellence	Independence
Confidence	Exhilaration	Influence
Connectedness	Experience	Inspiration
Contentment	Experimentation	Integrity
Contribution	Fairness	Intimacy
Co-operation	Faith	Intuition
Courage	Family	Joy
Courtesy	Fitness	Justice
Creativity	Forgiveness	Kindness

Knowledge	Religion	Standards
Leadership	Respect	Strength
Learning	Responsibility	Success
Love	Risk	Support
Loyalty	Romance	Tenderness
Nature	Self-awareness	Thrill
Nurturing	Self-discipline	Tolerance
Openness	Self-expression	Trust
Passion	Sensuality	Truth
Peace	Serenity	Understanding
Perseverance	Service	Virtue
Playfulness	Sexuality	Vitality
Pleasure	Sharing	Vulnerability
Politeness	Sincerity	Wealth
Pragmatism	Sobriety	Wellbeing
Purity	Spirituality	Wisdom
Reliability	Spontaneity	Wonder

Your attitude

Your attitude to life develops out of your experiences, and the way you think and feel, and is THE KEY to your success.

Here are some examples of positive and negative attitudes which will greatly affect the outcome of situations. Some of them affect situations so dramatically that they become self-fulfilling prophecies:

Negative	Positive
Where's the catch?	Where's the opportunity?
I'm better than you	I am equal to you
This will never work	I'll make this work
I'm not worth this	I am worth this
I've heard it all before	What can I learn here?
I can't do this	I can do this
What's wrong with this?	What's right with this?
I'll make a fool of myself	I'll learn something
I'm too old/young	I'm the right age

Your attitude colours how people perceive you.

Your attitude can warm the space between you and other people, and help them respond to you more positively. Optimistic, energetic people are promoted in preference to cynical, inflexible people. So – keep the drive and energy that you have going. If you've lost it – take action to find it again.

Your attitude is the filter through which you experience your life. You may not want it rose-coloured, but make it positive! Attitudes change depending on your relationships, the time of year, your time of the month, your level of motivation, the reward in view or changing events.

What would you say are your basic underlying attitudes?

Head messages

One way to pin this down further is to be aware of messages you send yourself. These messages are like a commentary or script playing in the back of your mind. They may not originally have been your messages. They may have come from elsewhere: parents, the media, friends, school. In which case, they are part of your conditioning.

> Elise:
> I've always been financially independent throughout my marriage by working freelance. It gives me a great sense of self-esteem and comes from my mother drumming into me 'Always stand on your own two feet!'

> Kwento:
> I always approach my work as a Transport Co-ordinator painstakingly and have to do it that bit better than anyone else around me. I think it comes from everyone in my teens telling me that as a Black woman I would have to be 10 times as good as anyone else to get anywhere at all.

Here are some head messages about:

- attitude — 'don't risk it – settle for what you have'
- older people — 'they'll be slow to pick this up'
- other women — 'why don't I speak up like Shona?'
- appearance — 'you can't look professional in smart casual'
- men — 'they don't share feelings'
- eating — 'clear your plate – food waste is bad'
- yourself — 'I'm too old/clumsy/slow/unfit/out-of-date'
- things that go wrong — 'they always come in threes'
- things that go well — 'it was only luck'

WHAT ARE YOUR HEAD MESSAGES?

Write down at least six of your head messages, and the effect they have had on your life so far:

MEDITATION

Close your eyes. Breathe slowly and easily and let go of any tension that you notice in your body. Let your mind focus on the words 'I am'. Imagine these words, hear them, see them, feel them.

Stay with the words and allow yourself a few minutes of quiet. Let go of any judgement of yourself and do not add any further words to make the sentence more complete.

When you start working with this meditation, it is better to focus for two minutes then stop. Then when you are able to stay focussed, deliberately extend the time by a few more minutes. Stop by making a clear and deliberate return to the present and then open your eyes.

Summary and action

In this chapter you have done a lot of work on yourself. This provides you with a launch pad for the more outgoing, practical skills chapters later in the workbook. Know yourself and value yourself so that you can become more fully yourself.

Action

What are you going to do now to build on the advantages of being you? What are you going to do to turn the disadvantages into advantages?

Here are some suggestions:

- I've never done bungee jumping. I'll try it on my holiday
- dealing with this new client is a stretch. I'll start on Tuesday
- this week I'll think the best of new people I meet
- tonight I'll ask Dad more about how it was working in France
- starting today, I'll note down new learning every night
- I'll pick up litter on the way to the bus tomorrow
- I'll have lunch with Jess tomorrow. That will give me a boost
- at the team meeting next week, each time I notice a problem I'll also suggest a solution

Write yours here:

Specific action   **By when?**

Profile *Sheree Axon*

Job Title: Director of Change and Programme Delivery
Organisation: NHS England

At the time of writing, which coincides with my 55th birthday, I have been thinking about my past working years and my contribution over the next phase of my life. Springboard was an instrumental 'pivot point' for me when I joined the NHS, and it continues to be very influential and inspiring to me and the many women I encourage to get involved.

My own story is, like many other women, defined by the need to have significant levels of resilience and endurance, whilst working hard to make the best of every situation, however difficult, challenging and unplanned it may be.

Born in East London, I started school in Tilbury and at age five, I had discovered my loathing of milk (issued at break times), my love of singing (a solo in a school play) and my love of books when I joined the library. By the age of 11, starting high school in what was then Rhodesia (now the country known as Zimbabwe), I had already attended four different schools in three different countries. I experienced a lot of change, always feeling an outsider.

My high school years in Rhodesia, suffering food and fuel shortages, war and unrest, taught me resilience, survival and making the best of things. By 16, I was at work, contributing to household funds, briefly with Barclays, then an apprenticeship with Holiday Inn, studying at Witwatersrand University in South Africa. It was a hard graft but at 21 I was the first female manager running a hotel in Zululand, surrounded by game reserves and pineapple plantations. There were many highs and lows. I learnt a lot about myself, but, with a failed marriage behind me, I returned to England looking for a new path and purpose.

I had some great experiences in my 'gap years' – working in recruitment in Norfolk, singing semi-professional in a rock band, backpacking and working in Norway, Germany and Israel. But something was missing – that real sense of direction and purpose.

I was then lucky enough to secure a role in the Norfolk Ambulance Service as a trainee personnel officer. This was a pivotal time for me; finally the right place, right people and right purpose. I discovered and implemented Springboard, despite accusations of it being 'sexist' because it focused on women. I still have my workbook; it's interesting reading even now. I developed professionally with HR qualifications and a Master's degree, using my research to set up a support system for staff affected by continuous exposure to stress, and I made friendships that endure today.

This important work in the NHS and the ambulance service that began nearly 25 years ago was the start of my journey on what has turned out to be the guiding purpose for me – improving services in the wider NHS and public sector, making it a better place to work wherever I can. I've been fortunate to work at every level in the public sector and government to make that a reality. My work has always been important to me: having a purpose, making a difference with integrity, honesty and real conviction.

It's clear now, looking back, that I put that purpose, and other people, first and that's not always been the best thing for me. I've realised there's a reason they tell you on aircraft to put on your oxygen mask before helping others. Now, as a widow with a teenage daughter, I can see that the choices I made to fix other's oxygen masks before mine have impacted on my health, wellbeing, resilience and sense of purpose. The good news is that there is still plenty of time in the next phase of my life to make different choices and decisions.

Springboard helps you discover your personal purpose and place – what it feels like to fix your oxygen mask before fixing someone else's and, best of all, you'll feel part of a community of people with a safe space to speak up. That's just the beginning of your journey, but it's a great first step.

Learning points

- Remember to look after yourself. You can't look after others if you neglect your own wellbeing.
- Find out what is important to you and what drives you and use that as your life compass; hold all your decisions up to it to see how they align.
- When times are tough you learn survival skills that will get you through, resilience, adaptability, humour, but these are equally useful in the good times, so remember they are always in your kitbag.
- Know what means home and go there to renew yourself.

NOTES

4

> *Above all, be the heroine of your life, not the victim.*
>
> Nora Ephron

What You've Got Going for You

Objective
- to build on everything you've got going for you for your future action

This chapter is important because

- you need to assess where you shine and where you need polish
- knowing where your strength lies helps you take the next step
- valuing yourself gives you the confidence to tackle things

Contents
- your achievements
- positive and negative forces
- strength in qualities
- your skills audit
- transferable skills
- your qualifications
- your assertiveness audit
- confidence
- summary and action
- profile of Noorhan Abbas

You have so many aspects of yourself that you could use to achieve your goals. Don't underestimate them. Put them to work for you.

Your achievements

Wherever you are on life's path, behind you are all your achievements and your mistakes too. In front of you are your unfulfilled dreams and ambitions.

What achievements in your life are you really proud of? Write at least six. Include any areas of your life – family, work, home, social, sports, hobbies, relationships, community activities, old achievements as well as recent ones.

1.

2.

3.

4.

5.

6.

7.

8.

9.

10.

What is there that you haven't achieved that you may still want to try to achieve? Don't worry at this point about whether it seems achievable or not.

1.

2.

3.

4.

5.

6.

7.

8.

9.

10.

We'll come back to these later.

Positive and negative forces

If you imagine your life as a journey, then what are the forces that are helping you move forward, making it worthwhile and preventing you from being stuck?

Melodie: (Positive forces)

My divorce has gone through and I'm in control of my own life again. I need a challenge – I feel under-used. I'm not afraid to try new things, perhaps a change in the type of work I'm doing. I'm keen to make new changes. I've got two very supportive friends. There's got to be more to life than this!

Jules: (Negative forces)

Not being brave enough to climb out of my comfortable rut. Don't want to upset my partner. Afraid of seeming selfish. I hate interviews. Men dominate engineering. Fear of making a fool of myself.

First list all the forces helping you here; everything inside you and outside you. Write down absolutely everything you can think of and ask family, friends or colleagues what they think and add their suggestions even when you don't fully agree with them:

What's holding you back?

Across your path there will be hurdles – they hold you back, deflect you, slow you down and may even stop you. Getting over them will take some effort on your part.

Jules has mentioned several that were important for her. List all the things that are standing in your way, internal and external, and maybe represent them visually by creating images or pictures (perhaps just colour and shape) of how they seem to you:

Taking control

The exciting and encouraging aspect of this analysis is to realise how much you can influence the hurdles that you've described. There are very few that are impervious to change. So few that we can identify them here:

- you cannot change your race
- you cannot change your age
- you cannot change your genetic inheritance

But you can change your ATTITUDE to these, and your ways of dealing with the prejudice in others.

You have limited possibilities of transforming:

- society generally
- your company/organisation
- your level of disability
- your gender

But you can change your ATTITUDE to these, by updating your information about them and being alert to changes. You have the ability to change everything else – if you want to.

Write down things that you want to change about your attitude to yourself:

Strength in qualities

Knowing your qualities and strengths helps you:

- be confident
- choose appropriate goals
- know when you can achieve goals
- see which situations you will handle well

List your strengths – the things that you feel are your POSITIVE QUALITIES – in the left-hand box. Fill it right up; be as specific as you can. If your mind has gone a complete blank, talk to your partner, friends, boss and colleagues to get their ideas on what your positive qualities are. Remember also positive qualities that you have had in the past and may not have displayed recently.

Now do the same with your weaknesses in the top right-hand box. You will be filling in the other box later. Make sure you fill up the left-hand box with strengths first!

Your strengths	Your weaknesses
	Strengths as partners

Strengths and weaknesses in partnership

When we ask women about their strengths and weaknesses they can always list many more weaknesses. That's why we've given you a bigger strengths box. We improve more by focusing on where we are already strong rather than finding ways to fix weaknesses.

> Yuna often felt disorganised, continually losing things and forgetting appointments. She described this as one of her weaknesses. Patience and determination were among her strengths. She realised that she often wasn't patient enough with herself, rushing on in life to the next thing. She decided that if she could use her determination to be more patient with herself she could reduce her level of disorganisation.

Now go back to your strengths and look at where you may be able to use them to help you counteract, overcome or reduce the effect of your weaknesses. You probably don't show that weakness all the time. What strengths are you using unconsciously when that weakness is overcome?

Return to your chart on page 80 and in the bottom right-hand box write down the potential 'strengths as partners' that you could draw on to counteract or reduce the effect of some of your weaknesses.

Ask someone who knows you well how they perceive you. Often it is easier for other people to notice your strengths, and how you use them, than it is for you to be aware of them, but remember that other people's views are just their opinions. They may not have it right – get a second opinion on any doubtful ones. You'll be asking someone else about the skills audit that comes next – you may wish to ask this question at the same time.

MEDITATION

Choose a quality of yours from the last exercise which is a strength that you know you have now or have had in the past. Sit quietly and allow yourself to relax by breathing calmly and rhythmically. Release any tension you feel in your body and then bring into your mind an occasion when you used that quality for positive results.

Think through the occasion in as much detail as you can and, if need be, run through the events in your mind two or three times until you have all the detail right, as if you were replaying a video or hearing a repeating audio track. Once you have captured all the detail of the positive way in which this quality helped you in the past, imagine that you are able to condense that quality down into a small sphere that you can hold in your hand. Then imagine yourself putting the sphere into your pocket, purse or handbag; somewhere that you will easily be able to reach it again when you need it.

Now bring yourself back into the room where you are, wriggle your fingers and toes and open your eyes.

If you want to, make a note here of anything you want to remember from the meditation.

Your skills audit

A skill is an ability to do something. You will feel more confident when you are doing things you are already skilled at. You can assess the level of your ability to do anything and if you have no skill or ability or not enough then you simply have a gap.

Like this:

The next pages have lists of skills for you to rate yourself. Of course, this will be your subjective rating, so, before you start, photocopy these pages a few times and seek ratings from your manager/colleague/close friend. This gives you a comparison and useful feedback. All of these skills can be related to home life as well as working life.

If you find some skills difficult to rate, try to think of a time in your home or work life when you might have used this skill, or discuss with a friend or colleague what they understand by the skill. The skills listed are general and so you may wish to think of situations where you use or have used them, e.g. having ideas in a team meeting even when it's not about your work.

There are gaps at the bottom of each category for you to add other skills important to you, such as technical skills specific to your work.

Rate yourself 1–5 as follows:

5 – *extremely good at this*
4 – *good at this*
3 – *OK at this*
2 – *not too good at this*
1 – *rubbish at this*

PLANNING SKILLS

Planning skills are about the future.

Having good planning skills minimises risks and gives a structure to whatever you want to make happen. They enable you to consider possibilities and make decisions. They use your creative and pragmatic qualities. Add your own ideas to the end of the list.

	1–5		1–5
gathering information	☐	setting objectives	☐
using my imagination	☐	anticipating	☐
forward thinking	☐	making decisions	☐
having ideas	☐	exploring and expanding ideas	☐
organising ideas	☐	assessing	☐
diagnosing	☐	interpreting information	☐
categorising	☐		☐
predicting accurately	☐		☐
estimating	☐		☐
budgeting	☐		☐
researching	☐		☐

Doing Skills

Doing skills are about the present. Having made your plan, they get you started and enable you to carry it out. They fall into three categories – in relation to yourself, other people, and things.

	1–5		1–5
using physical strength	☐	understanding instructions	☐
using dexterity	☐	giving instructions	☐
using software	☐	following instructions	☐
using co-ordination	☐	attending to detail	☐
motivating others	☐	prioritising	☐
influencing others	☐	using time	☐
initiating	☐	negotiating	☐
enthusing	☐	expressing feelings	☐
reading	☐	pacing	☐
writing	☐	seeing steps to be taken	☐
speaking	☐	organising resources	☐
calculating	☐	*Add relevant technical*	
observing	☐	*skills here:*	
using spatial awareness	☐		☐
operating equipment	☐		☐
decision making	☐		☐
following plans	☐		☐
taking risks	☐		☐
responding flexibly	☐		☐

KEEPING-GOING SKILLS

Keeping-going skills enable you to sustain action, and also enable you to enjoy things.

	1–5		1–5
knowing when to stop	☐	having fun	☐
knowing when to keep going	☐	speeding up	☐
encouraging yourself	☐	slowing down	☐
encouraging others	☐	changing plans	☐
laughing	☐	finishing things	☐
creating – words, music, etc.	☐	seeing the big picture	☐
listening	☐	resolving conflict	☐
counselling	☐		☐
coaching	☐		☐
helping	☐		☐
using your intuition	☐		☐

EVALUATING SKILLS

Evaluating skills are about getting the best from the past. They enable you to learn, make decisions and make better plans next time.

	1–5		1–5
assessing objectively	☐	reviewing	☐
measuring results	☐	adapting	☐
comparing results	☐	decision making	☐
observing objectively	☐		☐
letting go	☐		☐
stepping back	☐		☐
drawing conclusions	☐		☐
gathering information	☐		☐

What does it mean?

Got more going for you than you thought? Got less going for you than you thought?

Check that your modesty isn't preventing you boasting a bit or that the perfectionist in you isn't stopping you being satisfied with something that is less than perfect.

How does your own rating compare with that of your manager/colleague/friend? Do they rate you differently?

Use their rating to challenge your own, as they may assess you more accurately than you assess yourself. Who's got it right?

You can find more information on how your unique blend of skills could match with particular jobs or careers by doing a Skills Health Check at https://nationalcareersservice.direct.gov.uk/

Use this space for your notes of things you've learnt from this exercise:

Everyone has a talent. What is rare is the courage to follow the talent to the dark places where it leads.

Erica Jong

87

Transferable skills

The use of skills is severely limited by putting technical or professional labels on them which lock them into a particular profession. Assessing them under broader headings gives you more flexibility to transfer them to another form of work.

A good administrator can be described as 'just an Admin Assistant' or as being very skilled at:

understanding instructions	getting on with people
making decisions	interpreting information
using dexterity	using technology
using co-ordination	pacing
using visual awareness	breaking things down
using time	organising resources
attention to detail	organising people
working to deadlines	assessing
negotiating	encouraging themselves
influencing others	encouraging others

Transferring your skills

Women, particularly those who've had a career break or who are not in paid employment, tend to underrate their skills or not recognise how transferable they are. Make sure you don't do this.

- the skills used by a call centre worker will transfer into any job dealing with people
- planning and buying for a family can be translated into skills needed by a Retail Buyer or Project Manager

> Danielle:
> My Dad died in his 50s of heart disease. I was worried about my future health so I joined the Couch to 5k scheme via an NHS app. I started to encourage colleagues to jog with me at lunchtime. I really wanted them to get the same benefit as me and it helped my motivation too. I didn't realise how useful this was until my boss suggested I sign up as a mentor at work. I really enjoy encouraging people to have a go and progress at work and out in the park.

Transferring skills for Danielle meant that her ability to be supportive and encouraging was of benefit in a work context as well as for her running. Equally, the managing skills used by a mother to organise a football party for her nine year old transfer into project management.

Write down one aspect of what you do now in your work or current role. Then write alongside the transferable skills it gives you.

Log your transferable skills on page 283.

 Look at your skills in a transferable way – don't limit yourself.

Your qualifications

Qualifications are rather like cinema tickets. You have to have them to get you through the door, but once through the door everyone else has a similar ticket. They can also go against you, with people regarding you as over-qualified, so, either way, qualifications are a powerful message.

Qualifications
- can open doors
- can make it difficult to open doors
- give you credibility

- come in all shapes and sizes
- tell people what you have learnt
- tell people what you can do
- tell people what sort of person you are
- can be an asset or a hindrance
- may be helpful or unhelpful
- educational qualifications diminish in value as you get older
- professional qualifications are often highly valued
- people have got to the top without qualifications

 If you have qualifications – be proud of your achievements.

Turn to pages 280–282 and log your qualifications under the headings.

If you're thinking you haven't got much to write down, don't give up but think about what you may need. Some women have got to the top without formal qualifications, but employers are increasingly looking for qualifications.

The qualifications you had when you left school may have opened some doors. By the time you get to your mid-20s, school-leaving qualifications are no longer relevant: people are looking for more. Similarly, a degree may not mean as much in your 30s as it did in your 20s. You may need to gain more qualifications to suit what you now want to do.

Ways of gaining qualifications

Think about the many ways you can gain qualifications before making future decisions. Award-giving bodies are constantly increasing their flexibility. There are:

- full-time, flexi-time, part-time, block release and short courses
- distance learning, e-learning and Open University-style courses needing little or no time away from home
- evening, day and weekend courses
- fixed schedules and 'take as long as you like' programmes

- modular courses where you get time off in between
- ways to learn online with MOOCs and YouTube channels
- work based apprenticeships for all ages

Which qualifications?

You don't need any formal qualifications at all to start an Open University degree course. If, on the other hand, you have a PhD, you may still need a vocational qualification to achieve your next goal. Think about the wide range of qualifications before deciding which one to investigate further:

Vocational qualifications e.g.

- Heavy Goods Vehicle/Public Service Vehicle Licence
- City and Guilds Trade and Supervisory Qualifications
- Institute of Leadership and Management awards
- HND/HNC further education awards
- National Vocational Qualifications/Scottish Vocational Qualifications
- Police Sergeant's or Inspector's examinations

Academic qualifications e.g.

- GCSEs, A Levels, Scottish Highers and Advanced Highers
- BTEC certificates/diplomas for technical/business subjects
- degrees: –   Bachelor's: BA, BSc, BEd
  -         –   Master's: MBA, MA, MSc, MPhil, LLM, Med
  -         –   Doctorate: PhD, DPhil

Postgraduate and professional qualifications e.g.

- Membership of Institute of Mechanical Engineers
- Associate Chartered and Certified Accountant
- Approved Driving Instructor
- Inspector of Weights and Measures
- Farrier, Paramedic, Chartered Security Professional

There are hundreds of other qualifications to choose from. Take a look at **www.gov.uk/browse/education** for information on apprenticeships and further and higher education.

What qualifications do you want or need to get for your work?

What qualifications do you want to get for your own fun or satisfaction?

Will anyone give you any form of help in getting these qualifications? Your organisation may have a policy to support the gaining of qualifications that are directly related to your work – or unconnected with your work.

Find out if you qualify for support. If you don't know, ask your HR Manager or the person who deals with this in your organisation. If you are not working, or there is no support from your organisation, check other available sources of sponsorship from charitable trusts or even charitable friends. Government initiatives sometimes provide a source of funding. Some banks offer career development loans.

Your assertiveness audit

Assertiveness is such an important transferable interpersonal skill that we have devoted two chapters of this workbook to it, so you'll be getting a good dose of it later on. Meanwhile, fill in this questionnaire to assess your current level of assertiveness that you have got going for you.

Circle the a, b, c or d response to identify how you tend to behave in these situations. Complete the questionnaire quickly. Your first answers are usually the best and most accurate.

1. *You would prefer to have Christmas or a similar festival on your own with your partner/friend; your partner wants to go to their family. Do you:*

   a. imply that it's unfair and hope things will change?
   b. go to the family – anything for peace?
   c. say how you feel and what you would like?
   d. flatly refuse to go?

2. *You have just started to eat your main course in a restaurant. It should be hot but it's cold. Do you:*

   a. tell the waiter this isn't the item you ordered and order another dish?
   b. carry on and eat it?
   c. tell the waiter it's cold and ask for a fresh hot portion?
   d. point out that this isn't good enough and demand better?

3. *A friend or colleague circulates unwanted emails to you too often. Do you:*

   a. drop hints in polite replies?
   b. delete them and say nothing?
   c. explain the effect on you and ask for them to stop?
   d. fire off an angry email back?

4. An interview panel member asks a question that seems discriminatory to you. Do you:

    a. quip back a quick retort?
    b. answer as best you can?
    c. express concern about the question only if you feel OK with doing it?
    d. point out how wrong it is to ask such questions then refuse to answer?

5. When you are entering the car park and are about to reverse into a parking space another driver nips in and pinches the space. Do you:

    a. block the other car in?
    b. ignore it and find another space?
    c. tell the other driver how annoyed you are and ask them to move?
    d. give the other driver a piece of your mind for their rudeness?

6. Someone criticises your appearance at work. Do you:

    a. say something like 'Well I'm just keeping to the dress code'?
    b. blush and say nothing?
    c. check what is specifically being said and judge for yourself?
    d. tell them it's none of their business?

7. You are asked to work late for the third time this week. You already have another appointment to go to. Do you:

    a. give what you think is a cast-iron reason for not staying?
    b. try saying 'no' and end up staying?
    c. say 'no' firmly and say when you have to leave for your other appointment?
    d. complain that it's the third time this week and say a definite 'no'?

8. *Your family don't seem to be listening when you try telling them about your plans for Saturday. Do you:*

    a. say something like 'Well if anyone's interested I'm ...'?
    b. keep quiet?
    c. say how you feel and that it's important to you to tell them about your plans?
    d. talk more loudly?

9. *When you keep quiet in a situation, is it because:*

    a. you know the silence will have an effect?
    b. you are too upset or frightened to speak?
    c. you have nothing to say?
    d. you're sulking?

10. *You feel angry or upset. Do you:*

    a. let people know in a roundabout way?
    b. keep quiet?
    c. try to say how you feel and be specific?
    d. explode*?*

Write in the boxes how many times you answered a, b, c *or* d:

a [ ]   b [ ]   c [ ]   d [ ]

Mostly b

Your behaviour tends to be passive.

Mostly c

This shows that you tend to be assertive, but check that you actually do the things you say you do. Sometimes it is easy to see what the best solution is on paper but a more passive or more aggressive response may slip out in the heat of the moment.

Mostly a's and d's

Your behaviour tends to be aggressive. Mostly *d* indicates directly aggressive responses; mostly *a* indicates responses that are indirectly aggressive and manipulative. Most people confuse assertive behaviour with aggressive behaviour, so it's not unusual to have a high score here.

What do you want to change about this pattern?

Confidence

The final part of this chapter is about confidence.

You may have discovered that, while you've got some things going for you, you lack the self-confidence to take the plunge and get on with it. Or you may feel you are lacking qualities and qualifications, and need the confidence to do something about it.

You may feel confident in work situations and lack confidence in social situations, or the other way round. Everyone's different.

Confidence means

- being able to start things feeling that you will do reasonably well
- you get on with what you want to do
- you feel that, whatever happens, you will be OK inside
- being able to have a go even if you're not sure of the outcome

Lack of confidence means

- you feel you can't do things
- you put off doing things until you feel more confident
- you have difficulty doing things
- you feel powerless or uncomfortable, or both
- you feel that whatever you do it won't be good enough
- even when you're doing things well, you feel like a bit of an imposter
- you don't even try

Over-confidence means

- you don't know your own limitations
- you undertake to do things you can't necessarily fulfil
- you are unrealistic

It may be that your reason for working through this book is to help build up your self-confidence. Knowing the situations and people who undermine your self-confidence may give you a clue to the goals you want to set yourself later on in this workbook.

If you are easily intimidated by more senior people, assertiveness skills may help. If you lack confidence when asked to speak in public, consider taking a course in presentation skills, or volunteer to say something small like making an announcement at a meeting or giving a vote of thanks to a speaker. Some people benefit from joining an organisation such as Toastmasters.

CONFIDENCE PEAKS AND TROUGHS

Identify yours here:

I am most confident when:	I am least confident when:
People who help me feel confident are:	People who contribute to my lack of confidence are:
How I can use the confidence I have:	What I can do to build my confidence is:

Use the situations and people who help your confidence as the foundation stones on which to build further confidence. When your confidence takes a knock, remember these situations and use your supporters.

Summary and action

In this chapter, you've looked at many of the things that you've got going for you. Assess your findings positively and enthusiastically, celebrate all the good things you've already got to help you reach your goals. In areas where you are disappointed or deflated, decide firstly whether it matters or not – nobody has everything – and if it does matter, decide what first step you will take to do something about it.

Action

What action are you now going to take to develop your skills, strengths, qualifications and confidence? Here are some suggestions:

- tonight research IT courses near home
- when I next see Laura tell her how she boosts my confidence
- ask my boss next week to explain their ratings of my skills
- say yes next time there is an opportunity for field work
- spend Friday on reception to learn more about their work
- finish my course assignment by the end of the month

Write yours here:

Specific action   **By when?**

Profile *Noorhan Abbas*

Job Title: PhD Student
Organisation: Lancaster University

When I moved with my husband and family to the UK from Cairo in Egypt, I had no idea that 16 years later I would be a full-time PhD student in a technology based subject with my children attending a rural village school.

Initially, arriving in a cold and cloudy UK was an unhappy culture shock. People expressed themselves very differently; I couldn't work or study as my children were too young; my husband, a hospital doctor, worked long hours and was on-call most of the time. I became depressed and my self-confidence was low.

Then two years later I discovered my true self as a result of supporting my son through many months of his treatment in hospital for brain cancer. I put all my energy into reading, entertaining him and enjoying his company. He is fully recovered now; playing football and doing karate. This experience led to my life changing. I trained as a volunteer to support child patients and their parents and then later I enrolled on a Master's course.

My self-confidence grew with positive comments and support from the hospital teams and from my university supervisor. He believed my passion and enthusiasm to learn and succeed would be enough to achieve my goals.

I was again alone with my husband working in a different county. He's always been supportive and we discuss my study plans and potential impacts on our family. Doing something for myself has massively boosted my self-esteem and positively affected our relationship.

Managing time efficiently to look after the children, meet study deadlines and volunteer at the hospital was stressful but I enjoyed every bit of the course. We moved again with my husband's job, which was difficult for the children, changing schools and leaving their friends. In my MSc I used artificial intelligence to build a comprehensive index for the Quran online. The computing and tech skills helped me secure a good job as a researcher/analyst with the Police Service in the new area and I started to build a new circle of friends.

I attended the Springboard programme and insights from this, with my enjoyment of learning and academia, led me to apply for a PhD. Despite learning about building self-esteem and self-confidence through Springboard I still had doubts about my application, as I was older than other candidates. My MSc supervisor encouraged me and offered to be a referee. After an interview, to my surprise, I was offered the scholarship.

My research is helping police officers to be more efficient by enhancing their use of specialised mobile phones. I want to have a positive influence/impact in the society that I live in. My Springboard learning has helped me share my knowledge through excellent presentations at major conferences. I also still meet regularly with my support network from the programme; I couldn't have managed all the stress of the PhD without them.

I am now half way through my PhD and have become a full-time student. I am enjoying the learning journey thoroughly. There will soon be two Doctors in my family and who knows what the future may then hold!

Learning points

- Take every advantage of opportunities and always say yes – all the time I spent with my son in hospital was really valuable for my learning and led to my volunteering role.
- If you focus on doing things that you love and have enthusiasm, life flows really easily and you will always bring your best energy to your tasks.
- Whatever your age and life stage you can always start a new career, learn more and continue to grow.

NOTES

" *Find a group of people who challenge and inspire you, spend a lot of time with them, it will change your life.* "

Amy Poehler

Who Have You Got Going for You?

Objectives
- to identify how other people may help or hinder you
- to maximise support from your relationships

This chapter is important because

- only a very few of us make it on our own
- you can encourage other people to support you

Contents
- how people influence you
- the roles people play
- networking and building your contacts
- summary and action
- profile of Anne Frazer

Making relationships that support you

None of us lives in a vacuum. You may be all too well aware of the influence other people have had on you, or you may feel that you've done it all on your own. Being aware of the effect of other people on you can help you find support.

How people influence you

The influence that other people have can vary enormously:
- directly or indirectly
- negatively or positively
- consciously or unconsciously

Influences that appeared negative at the time, in retrospect, can prove positive:

'Getting good grades and moving away to university was the only way I could think of to escape my overprotective and suffocating parents.'

'Returning to study after redundancy, I was able to embark on a really fulfilling career.'

Active goodwill

If you could think of everyone you are acquainted with, and research shows that we all potentially know about 500 people, they are likely to fall broadly into three categories along a scale of 'helpfulness'.

- 10% are people who will actively help you – no matter what
- 80% are people who aren't particularly interested in you, but would help if you took the initiative
- 10% are people who don't like you, or what you stand for, and will actively hold you back or try to stop you

The 10% who are for you – they like you and will actively support you, give you ideas and contacts and encourage you. Keep them in the picture about your plans. You tweet, text, WhatsApp, email or ring each other quite often. They are probably your Facebook friends. You meet up and you feel good about your relationship with them.

The 10% who are against you – you won't win everyone over, so it may be a waste of time and energy trying to turn these people around.

The huge majority of people you know will be part of the middle 80%. These people can be described as having 'latent goodwill' towards you. They may be part of your LinkedIn network. They do not lie awake at night worrying about you, but equally are not going to slip banana skins under your feet. They probably don't think about you at all! These people are important to you – it is your job to turn their latent goodwill into active goodwill. You'll have to take the initiative here.

Lily:
An old school friend used to work in IT before she took a career break. I'm thinking of setting up my own business and need to know about online marketing. I decided to pick her brains about how to go about it. She was very helpful, gave me lots of tips and questions to ask web designers and e-commerce providers. I now feel much more confident about talking to these experts and getting the best deal for my business.

 It's up to you to take the first step, to know which battles to fight, and which to leave alone.

The roles people play

A useful way of thinking about people is in terms of the role they play in our lives, while remembering that one person may play several roles – often all at once!

The next exercise is to help you identify the ways in which people influence or help you at present, and to identify any gaps. If you already have ideas for your future, think also about how they could help you take the next steps.

Write the names of people you know under each category and make a few notes about why they are there:

1 ENERGY GIVERS – PEOPLE WHO MAKE YOU FEEL GOOD

We all need these people – they give you the warmth and reassurance to keep going when life gets tough, and give comfort when you fail. Their warmth restores you. They are easy to be with. They boost your confidence because you know they are on your side.

2 ENERGY DRAINERS – PEOPLE WHO DRAIN YOUR ENERGY

These people don't realise the effect they have on you, but being with them either makes you feel ineffective and frustrated, or exhausted and apathetic. They may be lovely, well-meaning people, but they take away your energy to achieve your goals. They may be bright and chatty or dull and gloomy. They take up too much of your time and sap your confidence.

3 ROLE MODELS — PEOPLE WHO HAVE SET THE PRECEDENT

These are the people who have done what you are thinking of doing and against whom you may be compared. They can be a positive influence, such as opening up new areas for women in the world of work, or negative, such as setting standards of behaviour which you choose not to follow.

4 HEROES AND HEROINES — PEOPLE WHO INSPIRE YOU

These may be people you know personally and could also be people who you don't know – alive or dead, real or fictitious. They contribute to your sense of purpose and your determination, and help you see where your goals for the future lie or inspire ideas of who you may become.

5 GATEKEEPERS — PEOPLE WHO CONTROL YOUR ACCESS TO OPPORTUNITIES

These people control your access to training, information, resources, people, support and ideas, and they mostly like to have recognition for doing this. It may be their job to do so – Line Managers and HR Managers may fall into this category. Family and friends open and shut doors too. Gatekeepers can be helpful or unhelpful and can be more senior or more junior than you.

6 NEUTRAL PEOPLE — THOSE WHO WILL HELP IF YOU ASK THEM

These are the people who aren't particularly interested in you, but will help if you take the initiative. You will have to ask for their advice, ideas and information, but they will be quite happy to give it. This is likely to be a large category and may overlap with many of the others. They are not telepathic, so you will need to tell them what you want.

7 ENEMIES — PEOPLE WHO ACTIVELY OPPOSE YOUR PROGRESS

These people don't like you, or what you stand for, may resent your success or feel threatened by or jealous of what you're trying to do. You may not have anyone opposing you quite as strongly as this but you may know of people on the edge of this role. Enemies put you down, undermine the support you get from others and the confidence you build up.

8 GARDENER BOSSES, COACHES OR MENTORS — PEOPLE WHO GROW YOU

These are the bosses who have a reputation for giving people opportunities and for stretching them. After that it's up to you. Grab the opportunities they offer to speed up your development! Gardener bosses enjoy helping others to develop and grow – get all the support you can from them when you have one – and look for one if you haven't got one. Think also about others who coach or mentor you either formally or informally.

9 APPRENTICES – PEOPLE YOU ARE HELPING AND ENCOURAGING

Who are you opening doors for or helping up behind you? Who looks to you for encouragement and may regard you as a mentor or coach? Your relationship with them helps you to develop. Both in and outside of work, developing your successors may free you up to do new things.

> ‘ *Always remember that you are not the only one who has ever felt rejected, unloved and lonely at some time. Reach out and help someone else in trouble, and you could be amazed at the changes in yourself – and your life!* ’
>
> Anon.

HOW DOES THIS HELP?

Are you getting enough objective advice and feedback? Are you being challenged enough? Are you getting enough support? Do you need a mentor or coach? Is your access to information and ideas wide enough, or are all your ideas coming from one area?

To get the best out of the previous exercise, think about these questions:

Which, if any, categories predominate?

How do you feel about this?

Which, if any, categories are totally missing?

What do you want to do about this?

Where is your main help and support coming from?

Who is giving you constructive feedback?

How will you deal with those who are hindering you?

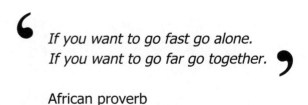

If you want to go fast go alone.
If you want to go far go together.

African proverb

MEDITATION

Relax and release any tension in your body. Allow your breathing to settle and take you to a deeper state of relaxation. Breathe evenly and deeply.

Think about the qualities of a person who is really supportive. You may use a real person who has already supported you, a famous person, someone from films or fiction or a mixture of several people who, if rolled into one, would be the most supportive person that you can imagine.

Take your time really getting a sense of that person. Now imagine yourself having a brief conversation with them to ask for their support for the changes that you are going to make in your life.

Imagine that they reply very positively, also remaining grounded in the reality of what you may embark on next. So they will gently challenge you as well as support you if it seems as if you need to be challenged.

Close by assuring yourself that if you ever want to get support or advice from this imaginary person all you have to do is to sit or lie quietly and bring them into your awareness.

Open your eyes and bring yourself gently back into the present by counting how many different colours there are around you. (This is simply to make sure that you are back in reality after being in your imagination.)

FURTHER OPTIONAL WORK

To take this further, you can approach this exercise in reverse and explore the roles that you play in other people's lives. Are you being cast in the same role too often? Do you want to change the balance of the roles you're in?

Networking and building your contacts

Here we are using 'networking' to mean a positive process of mutual support. Extending your contacts to give you greater access to ideas, people, support and opportunities is extremely positive and influential and the dramatic explosion in online networks makes this even easier. In the palm of your hand, via your smart phone, you now have access to people anywhere in the world, so, in addition to the people you actually know, you can add an additional category of people who can help you without you ever meeting or even speaking to each other.

The theory of 'six degrees of separation' is that all of us are only six (or fewer) contacts away from anyone else in the world. So, in theory, you can be in touch with virtually anyone, given a bit of effort and imagination.

Your own network is simply everyone you know. If you extend that to everyone they know, your network multiplies many times again.

Sometimes we know people because we like them just for their own sake and sometimes because of an existing connection or a mutual interest e.g. family, neighbours, fellow professionals, members of online networks/ forums, people involved in the same sports, activities, hobbies or interests.

The more people you know, the greater your flexibility to achieve your goals. You do not have to become friends with everyone; indeed you may not even like them. Knowing people is rather like travel – it broadens the mind!

Formal networks

In addition to getting to know people informally, there are hundreds of more formal networks, ranging from Parent Teacher Associations, through to professional institutes and women's groups. See Chapter 14 for details of some of these networks. This is just the tip of the iceberg, so do some detective work and you will find many more. If there isn't a branch of what you need in your area, start one! Most of these groups started with one or two women getting together casually, and building it up from there.

How Well Are Your Contacts Working?

Use the grid on the next two pages to form your action points from this chapter:

	What is working well?	What action to improve?	By when?
Generally			
Up-to-date contacts			
Out-of-date contacts			
Online networks			
Meeting people very different to you			
Meeting people who know things that are helpful for your future			
At work			
Your email/phone contacts			
Your face-to-face contacts			
Contacts in other departments			
Contacts outside your organisation			

	What is working well?	What action to improve?	By when?
Outside of work			
Your email/phone contacts			
Social networking contacts			
Your face-to-face contacts			
Interest groups, clubs, societies, church			
Who you send cards to for birthdays and festivals e.g. Christmas, Divali, Eid, New Year, Hanukkah, etc.			
Formal networks/ organisations			
List the ones you belong to and then assess them			

Don't underestimate people – they mostly want to help.

Summary and action

In this chapter, you've taken a brief look at the role and influence of other people in your life, and how you can build on that positively. You have already been networking but you may want to do this more consciously in the future.

Action

What other action will you take now to help people to help you?
For example:

- update my LinkedIn profile next week
- go to our internal women's network next month
- next meeting, ask my mentor about their career path
- call Olivia tonight; I've neglected her since her birthday last year
- ask my boss for straight feedback at our next catch-up
- talk to Paul on Monday about how roles in his team differ from mine
- delete ancient contacts from my email on Friday

If anything is not included in the table above, add it here:

Profile *Anne Frazer*

Job Title: Senior Finance Consultant
Organisation: Schools Business Service

A fairly normal family life in Derby was abruptly halted when I was six and my Dad was killed in a road accident. Within two years my three (much) older siblings had left home and we were living on a smallholding in rural Cornwall after my mother married an elderly retired farmer. Everything about me was different from my school friends. I tried to change to fit in, but never quite managed it. I realised it wouldn't always be like that and that my Mother too faced and dealt with many fears as she built her new life.

By my early 20s I was married with two daughters, living in the North Midlands where we'd bought our first house. It was the late 1980s; we narrowly avoided repossession with our tiny single income pitched against rocketing interest rates. Not the best situation to then have two more children – sons this time.

Life now consisted of: eat (maybe), sleep (possibly), repeat (definitely). The legacy of being young parents with few parenting skills and no family support was to lead to conflict and difficult decisions later in life. We just about managed financially with extreme thrift; make do, mend or do without. We were determined to avoid parental censure for the situation we'd created.

We finally climbed out of the financial hole, moved and extended to accommodate our teenagers. Living in a building site with the hurly-burly of our everyday life family where I had too many roles, I also had to deal with serious wider family pressures and hold down a job. I was completely overstretched.

Life was a chaotic spiral, plunging my husband into depression, fracturing his relationship with the children; our eldest daughter also went through a particularly challenging phase and to prevent myself from a complete break-down I made the awful decision of sending her (just 17) to live with my sister. I don't know how I got through that time; I just put on my 'best' face and 'got on' with things but it knocked a hole in our marriage. Even though we had been everything to each other I learned I could only rely on myself.

My eldest daughter didn't speak to me again for almost three years. Her school was incredibly supportive to both her and us as a family. Eventually she got back in touch and we began to make repairs. My husband seemed unable to do this, his relationship with my second daughter was also strained, but the last straw came when he threatened my eldest son with violence. He'd nearly lost me my relationship with one of my children; now here he was putting another in jeopardy. I couldn't let it happen and I had to leave.

I didn't think I would make it; I really didn't. We'd been together all my adult life; I was devastated and terrified. Once again I just 'got on with it', rented a house, took a second part-time job, nurtured myself and said 'yes' to whatever was on offer, including volunteering and social activities.

And now ... 8 years on, well, you wouldn't recognise me. My relationship with my kids is incredible; it's the most important thing in my life. They are all wonderful people and I am honoured to be their friend as well as their Mum. I've climbed the career ladder, from working in admin to presently a finance consultant. I've moved cities and, at 50, have taken on a mortgage on a flat in Bristol, where I am building a new life. I started to run and learnt to swim and now do triathlons. I have taken control of my diabetes by changing my eating habits. I am fitter, healthier and happier than I have ever been.

Learning points
- Treat your own happiness as if it were another person and nurture it with as much care and attention as you would lavish on a life partner.
- Be grateful – every day – all the time. We have so much to be thankful for.
- Be clear on what is important to you. That will give you the strength and insight to make life's difficult decisions.
- You are NEVER incapable of making a new start, new friends and new relationships.
- You are a precious individual and are enough for the world just by yourself.

NOTES

6

> *Instead of looking at the past, I put myself ahead twenty years and look at what I need to do now in order to get there.*

Diana Ross

Setting Your Goals

Objectives
- to build on your successes
- to set your goals

This chapter is important because

- goals give you a sense of direction
- goals keep you moving
- goals determine what you do next
- goals channel your energy

Contents
- goals
- think-through questionnaire
- building on your successes
- how do you want your life to be?
- setting your goals
- is it worth it?
- what are you waiting for?
- summary and action
- profile of Sally Fox

In this chapter you will be setting your goals, drawing on the work you've already done. The goals can be as ambitious or cautious as you wish, as personal or work-related as you wish, as public or private as you wish. People who set and document goals and take action are generally happier and more satisfied with their life than those who don't.

Goals

- help clarify your thoughts
- get you started
- save time
- give you the impetus to make changes
- are not set in concrete and can be changed!

Some people feel uncomfortable about setting goals because:
- it seems like tempting fate
- if they don't reach them, they'll feel a failure
- if they're a success – what next?
- they'd rather just let life happen to them
- they're too busy
- they don't have the confidence

How do you feel about setting your goals?

Think-through questionnaire

Life for many women is rather like doing a circus balancing act while juggling at the same time! For those setting out on adult life there are so many options to think about and choices to make. Older women have to take account of the consequences of many previous decisions. Take as much time as you need to think about the questions that are important to you. The questions are designed to help you think about the different aspects of your life. Use them to clarify your thoughts and spark off ideas to help you in your goals. Skip the sections that don't apply to you.

Money matters

Money matters a great deal to some and not at all to others. Consider:

- do you have your own income?
- if so, how well does your income match your outgoings?
- how do you feel about the difference?
- are you the main or only source of household income? What does this mean to you?
- do you have, or are you considering having, a mortgage?
- are you repaying a student or other loan?
- how much more do you want to earn?
- how much less could you manage on if you really needed to or wanted to?
- how much money do you want to earn long-term?
- what about a pension? Do you have one? Is it the best one for you?
- do you have any savings or investments? Do you know the best approach to save or invest for your future?
- what if you became ill or couldn't work for a long time?
- do you need help to sort out your debts?

Work circumstances

Are you in paid employment? Are you looking for paid employment? How do you feel about working/not working in paid employment?

How do you want to work?

- full-time?
- part-time?
- flexi-time?
- job-sharing?
- self-employment or contract working?
- teleworking from home?
- voluntarily?

How prepared are you to move for work?
- what daily travelling are you prepared to do?
- how far would you move for the right opportunity?
- how much does your current pension scheme (if you have one) influence your decision to change work?

If you are thinking of starting your own business, or already have one, consider:
- how far down the track are you?
- what is the nature of your product or service?
- what market are you in?
- who specifically are your customers?
- what do they buy now?
- who are your competitors?
- how will market trends affect your business?
- how will you cope if your income is irregular?

Living on your own

If you are living on your own what do you think/feel about it?
- is it out of choice, or through circumstances?
- are you concerned about it or maybe never think about it?
- is it recent, temporary, longer term or permanent?
- what do you enjoy most about living on your own?
- what do you like least about living on your own?
- how long do you want to go on living on your own?
- do you want to change anything about living on your own?

How do others react to your living situation? Does it matter?
- what does your partner think about it (if you have one)?
- what do your friends/family think about it?
- what do those at your workplace think?
- what are the reactions of your neighbours?
- does anyone pressurise you to do something different?

What aspects of your life are affected by living on your own?
- how does it affect you financially?
- how does it affect you emotionally/mentally?

- how does it affect decisions you make about your future?
- what is the effect on your relationships?
- how does it affect how you use your time?
- how does it affect your behaviour at home and with others?
- how does it affect your decisions about holidays?

Living with others

If you are living with others also consider all the questions above for those living on their own.

What is your relationship like with the people you live with?

How is your life affected by those relationships?

Do you want to change anything about your living situation? If so what?

Considering a close partnership

If you are considering sharing your life with someone else, do you:

- want to access advice and support about making this decision?
- see it as a partnership for life or short-term?
- want to live with the person?
- know where you will live?
- want to share financial arrangements?
- want to make it a legal arrangement (marriage, civil partnership, trust deed)?
- want to have sex with them?
- feel your freedom being eaten away?
- know what you want out of the relationship?
- know what the other wants?
- know your doubts, fears and hopes?
- share your doubts, fears and hopes with the other person?
- love the person? (or are you in love? or both?)
- know how compatible or complementary your daily rhythms are?
- know how your work patterns relate to each other's?
- know what effect it will have on your social life?
- know how your track record with relationships is influencing you?

You don't need a significant other to lead a significant life.

Mandy Hale
The Single Woman: Life, Love and a Dash of Sass.

Being in a partnership

- how do you feel about your relationship?
- what aspects of life do you share – hobbies, friends, ideology, religion, politics, opinions, choice of films or music, etc.?
- how are you different or contrasting?
- how much respect does your partner show for you?
- to what extent does your sex life satisfy you?
- to what extent do you tolerate verbal, emotional or physical abuse?
- what financial arrangements do you have – separate or joint bank accounts, credit cards, etc.?
- how do you share all the expenses: equally? Proportionate to your income? Pool everything and treat it as if it's one income?

If your partner earns less than you or is not in paid employment, do you:

- treat all income as joint?
- make clear the differences?
- try to compensate by paying for things quietly or secretly?
- never mention it?
- feel OK about it – or not OK?
- know how your partner really feels about it?

If you earn less than your partner or are not in paid employment, also look at the questions above.

If you both work

What comes first?

- your work?
- your partner's work?
- your relationship with each other?
- something else?

What is your attitude to your own work?

- essential financially?
- unimportant for your fulfilment as a person?
- necessary for your development as a person?
- gets in the way of your relationship?
- enhances your relationship?
- stops you being effective in other roles?
- helps you cope with other roles?

What is your partner's attitude to your work?

- essential financially?
- unimportant for your fulfilment as a person?
- necessary for your development as a person?
- gets in the way of your relationship?
- enhances your relationship?
- stops you being effective in other roles?
- helps you cope with other roles?

How mobile/flexible are you and your partner?

- will move for your own work?
- will move for your partner's work?
- happy to be away for short / longer spells?
- happy for each other to be away for short / longer spells?
- whose work takes priority?

Also consider the questions about your attitude to your work, flexibility/mobility and what comes first if you are living by yourself, single or not in a partnership or relationship.

What about holidays?

- have them together?
- have them separate?
- it varies?
- don't have them/no time/can't afford them?

How long do you see your partnership lasting?

- forever?
- for quite some time?
- ending soon?

Considering starting a family (having your own or adopting or fostering children)?

- how do you feel about it?
- how does your partner (if you have one) feel?
- what size family do you want?
- how will having a family affect your life generally (financially, practically, emotionally)?

What will be the effects on your work of having children?

- types of work?
- mobility?

What arrangements will be needed for times of ill health?

Who will take what amount of time off around the birth (or adoption)?

Will you and/or your partner take a career break/parental/adoption leave?

How might a break affect:

- your career?
- your life with the child(ren)?
- your partnership?

What arrangements are needed for childcare?

How does being a working mother appeal to you?

What do you enjoy or look forward to about being a working mother?

What if you are unable to have children?

- how might you feel?
- what help will you seek?
- when will you give up trying?
- if unable to have a child will you consider adoption or fostering?
- if unsuccessful in adopting/fostering how might you feel?

Without children?

- is this a conscious choice?
- how do you feel about it?
- what are the benefits and drawbacks?
- how do other people treat you as a result?
- what might change this situation?

Already have children or step-children?

Who supports the child(ren) financially?

If you are a working mother, how is that for you?

How do/would you cope with the child(ren) or your partner in the event of:

- illness in the family?
- short spells away for work?
- longer spells away for work?

Who cares for your child(ren) after school and in the school holidays?

If your child(ren) is (are) under school age, how happy are you with your childcare arrangements? Who arranges childcare?

Who does the 'thinking' about how the child(ren) are looked after?

What do you need to do to improve things?

Does your child(ren) have any disability-related or special educational needs?

How does this affect your life?

If you share parenting with a partner who does not live with you how does that affect you?

How is your relationship with your child(ren) changing as they grow up?

How do you feel about your child(ren) leaving or having left home?

How does having (a) grown-up child(ren) affect you?

If you are a grandparent, or have caring responsibilities for your grandchildren, how does this affect you?

Dependent relative?

What effect does this situation have on your life?
- financially?
- emotionally?
- in terms of time?
- in terms of mobility?

What needs does your relative have?

How much are you able to meet the needs yourself?

How are the rest of the needs met?

What support services are available to you?

What further support do you still need?

What changes do you foresee in the immediate future?

How could an organisation's career break scheme help?

Friendships

After partners and family, friendships are our most important and influential relationships. When thinking about your friendships do you:

- feel happy, uplifted and valued or anxious and inadequate?
- have too many, too few or the wrong sort of friends?
- have a balance of Facebook or social network friends and real friends?
- have acquaintances rather than friendships?
- have friends who manipulate or belittle you?
- worry about what your friends think about you?
- worry about what your family think about your friends?
- consider some are one-sided?
- have many friends similar to you?
- have a diverse group of friends – different genders, ages, life stages, jobs, races, religions, interests, nationalities, outlooks?
- know you can rely on them or think they rely on you?
- spend enough, not enough or too much time with them?
- devote more time to social networks than to real life friends?

How are your attitudes shaped by your friendships?

Do you have a mixture of recent friends and those you have known a long time?

If you work (or volunteer) do you have friends in your workplace? Or not?

How do your friendships affect your relationship with your partner (if you have one) and how does your relationship with your partner affect your friendships?

What opportunities do you have to make new friendships?

- through or at your workplace or work activities or volunteering?
- via other friends or social networks?
- when attending activities or events?
- by being involved in hobbies or interests?

What do you want to be different about your friendships?

Do you have friendships that are not working? What do you want to do about them?

Work/life balance

We all need to balance our paid or unpaid work with other activities. And if you don't work, whether or not by choice, your wellbeing is supported by involvement in different types of activities which can also provide structure. Do you:

- not have time for any of that; there are too many other pressures?
- think that just coping with life is enough?
- prioritise and make regular time for hobbies or interests?
- not have any interests or hobbies outside work and family?
- want to have time for interests or hobbies outside work and family?
- feel like you have too much time to fill?
- have to-do lists for interests and hobbies as well as work?
- struggle to fit in everything you want to do?
- want to develop new interests or find new hobbies?
- feel finding a job or a new role is the only thing you have time for?

Do you do:

- things alone and with other people?
- activities that are mentally challenging?
- physical activity?
- things outdoors and indoors?
- activities with your children, partner, friends?
- relaxing things and stimulating things?
- engage with others in virtual reality and in real life?

What do you do to use and develop your creativity?

Do you want to be fitter, stronger, more flexible or just less tired or more engaged?

Do you want to develop a skill or technique further?

Are you learning new things, getting involved in new activities as well as doing things that you are good at or know well and are comfortable with?

What aspects of your work/life balance need attention?

Philosophy of life

Everybody has one, whether it is a deeply held spiritual or religious belief or a catchphrase you run your life by, such as as 'Always be useful' or 'Life is too short for perfection'. It may not be something you consciously think about.

- what is your philosophy of life?
- what is your faith, religion or spiritual belief?
- if none, what is your view – agnostic, atheist?
- do you follow any other particular path or guiding principles?
- what are you looking for or hoping for in life?
- what are your views about death?
- have you made a Will? If not, why not?
- how much does all of this influence your daily life?
- do you have a Living Will or have you given anyone Powers of Attorney?

WHAT DOES ALL THIS MEAN?

You have now reviewed some of the personal circumstances of your life which affect your decisions for the future. Jot down here what has come out of this:

What surprises were there (if any)?

What questions needed the most thought?

What needs more thought before you set your goals?

What do you need to discuss with others before you set your goals?

What do you want to change?

Discuss any issues that have arisen from this think-through questionnaire with the people involved or someone who can help you digest the questions and answers that have been provoked.

Building on your successes

Before you set your goals, one more aspect will influence them – your track record and view of success. Whenever you feel successful, it boosts your confidence and spurs you on.

What does success mean to you?

Jot down ideas of what success is for you – add at least five ideas:

Success is
Success is
Success is
Success is
Success is
Success is
Success is
Success is
Success is
Success is

WHAT DOES IT MEAN?

Each woman has her own personal blend of definitions of success. Check that yours are specific, e.g. to write 'success is being happy' is very vague – what specifically do you mean by 'being happy'? How do you recognise it, describe it, define it?

Notice how many of them you are already achieving.

My definition of success for me:

How do you want your life to be?

You may already be very clear about what you want to do with your life, how you want your life to be, what your goals are (that may be why you're working with this workbook), but if you're not, consider this approach.

The Wheel of Life

Your life is made up of many parts. When these parts are out of balance it can lead to feelings of unhappiness, frustration and discontent. This may be the reason you have picked up this workbook. By assessing your level of satisfaction and happiness with each part of your life individually you can start to get ideas about where you can set goals.

The Wheel of Life invites you to rank how happy or satisfied you are with each part of your life. Some you have already considered. It's not about having a perfect score in each area, but noticing where things are out of balance and need attention, where dissatisfaction in one part of your life affects other parts.

> Shirley:
> I worry every month about having enough to pay the rent. It's really difficult to find a flat here and I don't want to risk losing mine. So I always volunteer when there is overtime, which is mainly at weekends. My friends are going to an event about nutrition on a budget and I'd love to join them. It's on a Saturday morning, though, so I think I'll have to miss out. It's a pity. I hope they understand.

133

The Parts of Your Life

In the circle below there are sectors relating to each of the parts of your life. We've given titles to the six most important and left some blank sectors so you can add your own. If you prefer you can divide the sectors further and make smaller parts or rename all of the sectors to suit your life. Do whatever seems right to describe your life.

Give each sector a score from 1 to 10, where 10 is a high score, as to how happy or satisfied you are with that part of your life. Draw a line across the sector at that score or colour in or shade the sector from the centre up to that number.

When you have done this for all the sectors you have a picture of your overall level of satisfaction in each part of your life.

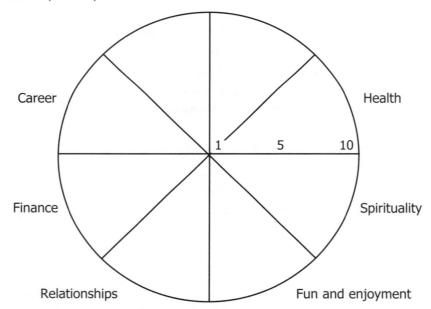

Career

Career relates to your job, paid or unpaid employment, volunteering, studying, education or whatever you have chosen as your field of work.

Finance

Finance relates to your overall financial position or level of financial security. Balancing your income, salary, wages, benefits, bonuses, savings, investments, pension with your outgoings, expenses, costs, mortgage, rent, what you pay for everyday items, holidays, treats or luxuries.

Relationships

This relates to all your connections and interactions with people. Think about family, friends, colleagues, acquaintances, people you live with, as well your relationship with your partner if you have one.

Fun and enjoyment

This relates to your personal interests and hobbies, cultural and social activities you are involved in for pleasure and relaxation. Activities that may relieve the stress you feel in other parts of your life.

Spirituality

This relates to observation of, growth in, practising or deepening of your philosophical, religious or spiritual beliefs, faith or doctrines. It relates to having or following a purpose or direction.

Health

This relates to your health and wellbeing, your levels of physical, mental and emotional fitness, your stress levels, how your health affects your daily living.

Here is an example of how your Wheel of Life might look.

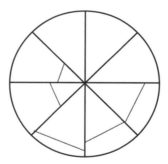

HOW DO YOU FEEL?

How do you feel about the balance in the parts of your life? Where you have given a low measure of happiness or satisfaction it's an area of your life for which you can start to set goals. And if all your scores are right for you then your goal becomes how to keep it that way!

What parts of your life will you choose to set goals in first? Will it be:

- the one with the lowest score?
- the one with the highest score?
- the one that has the biggest effect on the other parts?
- the one that seems most urgent?
- the one that seems easiest?
- the one that seems most important for your happiness or satisfaction?

 Everyone's dream can come true if you just stick to it and work hard.

Serena Williams

The dream/reality gap

Your Wheel of Life represents the reality of your present. We all imagine or dream how life could be in the future. Between the dreams of the future and the reality of the present there is often a gap. Setting goals allows you to bridge that gap. If the gap seems very big or insurmountable then it puts people off trying. When you look at the gap you can:

- find choices where there appears to be no choice
- look for the first simple steps to take you in the right direction
- challenge your assumptions about your constraints

 You have much more freedom than you think.

Setting your goals

Set whatever goals you want to:

- short-term and long-term
- serious and more light-hearted
- connected with all parts of your life or just one
- just for you and involving other people
- outrageous and conventional
- upfront and secret

- really big goals and smaller ones
- within your current organisation and outside it
- within the familiar and going out into the unknown

One good tip is to set a mixture – it will make life more interesting, and when you get stuck with one you can take action on another.

> *To anyone who has a dream, I say follow that dream.*
> *You are never too old. It's never too late.*

Susan Boyle

In setting your goals make them really specific and watertight by asking yourself the following series of questions about each one.

Is it stated positively?

Have you said what you want, what you would rather have instead of what you don't want? This gives you focus and a direction to move towards and you need to be really clear, not vague. If your goal is to have a better salary it's best to state an exact figure you are aiming at. If your goal is to worship more regularly it's better to say how often you want to attend your place of worship.

Do I want this for myself? Does it rely on me?

You'll be more likely to be successful with your goal if your drive to achieve it comes from within you and you are responsible for making it happen. This is better than for example setting a goal to eat healthily because your partner thinks you should or to decide to have the monthly budgets completed on time when they rely on data provided by a colleague.

How will I know when I've achieved it?

Be able to describe in detail what it will be like once you have achieved your goal. What will you be doing? What will you see, hear and feel once the goal is achieved? If your goal is to reduce stress how will the absence of stress actually feel? If you want to spend more time with your children what will you be doing in that time? What will you hear when you are with them? What will the expression on their faces be?

What is the context for achieving this goal?

This is fine tuning of your goal, getting really clear on the details of where, when, how and with whom. If your goal is to buy a house, in what time-frame will you make purchase? Where will the house be? What is your budget? How will you finance the house? Will you buy it alone or with others? If you want to learn the tango, who will you dance with, how and where will you get tuition, how long will it take to learn? Do you want to be good enough to win a competition or just to get across the floor without tripping up your partner?

What resources do I need?

This starts to drill down into the nuts and bolts of what you need in order to achieve your goal in terms of people, knowledge, time, money, support, information, energy and so on. Once you've worked out what resource you need ask yourself if you already have it or if you know how to get it. If what you need comes from within then ask yourself 'When have I had this before, so I can draw on it again for this new goal?' If your goal will need resilience, how can you use a past experience of being resilient to help you have that resource again? If you want to insulate your loft what knowledge and equipment will you need and how will you get them?

Does this goal fit in with all aspects of my life?

This is the question that helps you avoid failing with your goal because it just doesn't work with the rest of your life. Ask yourself what is the real reason why I want this? What will I lose or gain if I achieve it? What will happen if I get it? What will not happen if I get it? What will happen if I don't get it? What won't happen if I don't get it? What will the consequences be for me and those around me if I am successful?

Whilst these questions may seem tiresome, they will really help you to have a laser sharp focus so you commit your time, energy and resources to the things that are really what you want.

> Mia:
> My goal was to do something to make a difference for refugees arriving in the UK from conflict zones. I had a job with a charity which sends school books, clothes and toiletries. I did this for a while and realised I would rather work more closely with refugees as people. I looked for opportunities and now I teach basic employment skills at my local refugee centre and I feel really fulfilled.

Mia's charity job achieved many of the things she wanted but her real motivation was to make a difference in her local area. By working for the charity she lost the local aspect of what she wanted.

Work through the charts on the next pages. They follow the six parts of your Wheel of Life and there are extra pages for the blank sections. Start with whatever seems the most important part of your Wheel of Life to address now:

- goals for your career
- goals for your financial situation
- goals in your relationships
- goals for fun and enjoyment
- goals related to your spirituality and belief
- goals for your health and wellbeing

In the first column put the overall goal – remembering to be really specific.

In the second column record what you need to pay attention to in response to the questions on pages 137–138.

In the third column write down the very first step(s) that you need to take to achieve your goal. The first step(s) should be small individual actions that will start you positively on the path towards your goal. Consider them your first Action Points connected with this goal.

Have a go – after all you're not carving in granite – it's just a bit of paper and you can always change it!

YOUR GOALS FOR YOUR CAREER

Goal	Pay attention to:	What is the first step?

YOUR GOALS FOR YOUR FINANCIAL SITUATION

Goal	Pay attention to:	What is the first step?

YOUR GOALS FOR YOUR RELATIONSHIPS

Goal	Pay attention to:	What is the first step?

YOUR GOALS FOR FUN AND ENJOYMENT

Goal	Pay attention to:	What is the first step?

YOUR GOALS FOR SPIRITUALITY AND BELIEF

Goal	Pay attention to:	What is the first step?

YOUR GOALS FOR HEALTH AND WELLBEING

Goal	Pay attention to:	What is the first step?

YOUR GOALS FOR ....

Goal	Pay attention to:	What is the first step?

YOUR GOALS FOR ....

Goal	Pay attention to:	What is the first step?

You've been thinking hard to complete this chapter, now take a moment to top up your energy.

MEDITATION – TO ENERGISE YOU

Find a quiet spot and sit down or lie down. Begin by breathing out through your nose a little bit extra on the next out-breath. Let your breathing settle and notice the difference in the air as it flows from your nose over your upper lip. It may be colder as it goes in and warmer as it comes out.

Now imagine your body being covered by the colours of the rainbow going from your head, where your goals and visions begin, to your feet which take you forward into action:

Start at the top of your head with violet.
Next imagine your brow with indigo or a very deep blue.
Then on to your throat with blue.
Going down further to your heart area with green.
Then place yellow just above your waist in your solar plexus.
Moving to orange in the area below your tummy button.
Finally to red in your genital area and on down your legs to your feet.

To finish, move decisively. If you are able to, move to sitting or standing from lying or sitting. Stamp your feet a few times or move your arms vigorously.

Is it worth it?

Having set your goals, look back at what you've written, think about the consequences of all the hard work you've committed yourself to and ask yourself the one last question: Is it worth it?

If the answer is 'No' then you have set inappropriate goals, set them too high or with inappropriate deadlines. Go back and amend your sheets until the answer is 'Yes', because the answer has to be 'Yes' for you to carry on.

Reaching 'Yes' means you've reached the point of commitment. It's one thing to write down goals and know what you want to do with them. It's another matter to get started and keep going. That takes commitment. Commitment:

- turns ideas into action
- changes wishes into intentions
- takes courage and determination
- has to be renewed each day
- means you put your time and energy into it

This is the point to take the plunge and commit to action or go back and work through earlier parts of the process again.

What are you waiting for?

- the children to leave home/start school?
- the boss to retire?
- to win the Lottery?
- someone to encourage you?
- someone to make it safe for you?
- to have more time/energy/money/motivation/space?
- to feel ready?
- someone to die?
- someone to give you permission or ideas?
- a kick or a push?
- a tipping point?
- to get your qualification?
- the perfect job?
- to stop feeling guilty?
- your muse or inspiration?
- to stop feeling frightened?

It's easy to stop yourself setting goals or taking steps to achieve them if you think you have a good reason not to do it now. There may be very valid reasons why you cannot do something now, but just check that it's a real reason and not an excuse.

You may be working through this workbook because you feel you don't have any goals, so if you *still* feel that you don't have a goal, then setting a goal becomes your goal.

One way to help your commitment to your goals is to share them with someone who will support and encourage you. Have a conversation with someone you can trust to strengthen your commitment.

 You have to do what you dream of doing even while you're afraid.

Arianna Huffington

Having done that – stop

You have now achieved what for many people is the most difficult part of personal development – setting goals. Having the imagination and the determination to decide what to do is half the battle.

Now you've decided what you're going to do, the next step is to find how to do it. Make the process enjoyable.

 Decide whether or not the goal is worth the risks involved. If it is, stop worrying.

Amelia Earhart

Before you move on, have a celebration – whatever you like. Award yourself a treat – an evening off, a long bubble bath, a walk with a special friend – anything!

It's important that you acknowledge the importance of what you've just done.

A JOURNEY OF 1000 MILES STARTS WITH A SINGLE STEP.

Lao-tzu

Summary and action

In this chapter, you've been asked to consider a great number of issues. You've thought about how satisfied you are with the different parts of your life, and you've set your goals.

Further optional reading

Look for inspiration in the biographies of others.

Action

What action will you now take to start achieving your goals? Take each goal, and decide ONE SMALL THING you will do over the next week to make a start.

 Nothing is too small to be a start.

Write yours here:

Specific action   **By when?**

Profile *Sally Fox*

Job Title: Incident Assessment Unit Manager
Organisation: Avon and Somerset Police

I joined Avon and Somerset Constabulary as an
Emergency Call Handler 16 years ago. I was a
19 year old with big dreams of a career in policing
driven by my passion for helping people and making a difference for
my community. At that time women were significantly under-represented in
senior roles and young women were not perceived as tomorrow's leaders.
High performance wasn't enough for me to get access to opportunities or
promotion; being male and over 40 would have helped me more.

Over the years I lost sight of my dreams and aspirations, resigned to
remaining in an operational role and focusing on motherhood and family life.
The culture slowly began to change; young women were challenging the norm,
taking up leadership positions and, following maternity leave and spending a
few years working part-time, I realised I wanted to be one of them. I just
didn't know where to begin.

Four years ago I turned to the Springboard programme for help, after hearing
of it from a colleague. I was at a cross-roads, struggling to see how I could
achieve my career ambitions and still be a good mother. Through Springboard
I gained the realisation that I didn't have to compromise my family to progress
my career; I could have both. I grew to understand myself better, overcame
my self-limiting beliefs and was inspired by the guest speakers. I started to
seize opportunities, empowered with confidence drawn from my new
knowledge and skills.

Since the course I have progressed rapidly in my career, had another child and
even managed to secure a promotion whilst on maternity leave. I have
consciously surrounded myself with positive role models and those
relationships have inspired me to drive my career forward. I am now working
as a senior police staff leader, managing a team of 140 police staff and police
officers.

It hasn't been easy. I found doubts creeping in as I juggled the demands of children and greater responsibility at work, battling my own confidence and struggling to make time for me. Now each time I question myself I come back to my lessons from Springboard and realise that I can do it and the only obstacle is me.

I am now an active advocate for women in policing and working mothers, joining with other senior women across the Constabulary to share our experiences, inspire, empower and support our next generation of female leaders. Our coaching and mentoring enables them to realise their potential and be the best that they can be. I am also proud to recently have become fully trained and accredited as a Springboard trainer within the Constabulary and love being part of such an empowering concept. The finest reward for my contribution is that today there is a much higher representation of women in senior leadership roles in policing.

Springboard has been fundamental to my career progression, enabling me to build and maintain my confidence and self-worth. Self-confidence is still sometimes a struggle in the face of new challenges and increasing demands in policing; imposter syndrome is my nemesis. I now recognise it, push it to one side and storm forward towards the dreams of the 19 year old me.

Learning points

- The thing most likely to be holding you back is yourself. You are the person who can make the most difference to you.
- Women supporting women is really powerful. Remember those coming after you and try to share your experiences to help them progress too. You don't have to formally coach or mentor someone to do this. Quiet words of encouragement work too.
- If your employer does not support you to have a career and have a life, find one that does. Everyone brings greater value to work through their non-working life.

NOTES

> *No-one can make you feel inferior without your consent.*

Eleanor Roosevelt

The Assertive You

Objective
- to equip you with knowledge and understanding of assertiveness
- to build your confidence and skills in being assertive

This chapter is important because

- assertiveness enables you to deal with difficult situations and makes communication more effective
- there are lots of misunderstandings about assertiveness
- you need to decide for yourself which situations you want to work on by behaving assertively so that:
  - your self-confidence increases
  - you work out and achieve your goals
  - you are properly understood
  - other people know exactly where they are with you
  - you are more open to receiving feedback
  - your relationships are based on reality rather than illusion
  - you stand a better chance of getting what you want
  - you feel better for expressing your feelings
  - you succeed with more difficult situations
  - you have fewer situations that are unresolved
  - even if you do not resolve a situation, you feel better for having spoken up

Contents

- what assertiveness is and is not
- fight/flight syndrome
- assertiveness in practice
- your assertiveness agenda
- how to be assertive
- how to get better at the ingredients
- finding the right words
- tone of voice and body language
- summary and action
- profile of Dr Anjana Khatwa Ford

What assertiveness is and is not

There is a spectrum of behaviour. We are all capable of behaving aggressively, passively and assertively.

Aggressive   Passive

Aggressive behaviour is

- getting your own way, no matter what
- getting your own point across at other people's expense
- getting people to do things they don't want to do
- being loud and violent
- interrupting others
- winning at all costs

Not all aggressive behaviour is obvious or direct. There is also indirect or passive aggressive behaviour which can be:
- conveyed in a polite way
- quiet and apparently inoffensive
- manipulating or tricking people
- ignoring people

- being silent or sulking
- using sarcasm
- putting people down
- inoffensive on the surface

Most people have a tendency towards one end of the spectrum rather than the other, and vary their behaviour depending on the situation and their feelings at the time.

Aggressive behaviour doesn't come from being over-confident – quite the reverse; it comes from lack of confidence and fear. Underneath the blustery bully is a coward. It may be difficult to believe, but the person who's having a go at you is a real person underneath, who's feeling just as scared or threatened as a person behaving passively.

Passive behaviour is

- keeping quiet for fear of upsetting people
- avoiding conflict
- saying yes when you want to say no
- always putting other people's needs first
- not expressing your feelings
- going along with things you don't like or agree with
- apologising excessively
- inwardly burning with anger and frustration
- being vague or appearing not to care – 'whatever'
- justifying your actions to other people
- appearing indecisive

Ever found yourself doing any of this? Many women find themselves using passive behaviour quite a lot. If so, you may have reached the point where you don't know what your views or feelings on a topic are, but somehow you have a vague feeling of dissatisfaction at being taken for granted or not taken seriously.

Passive behaviour stems from lack of confidence. Turning passive behaviour into assertive behaviour will gradually build your confidence.

 Assertiveness is about building your own self-respect and respecting other people.

Assertive behaviour is

- being open and honest with yourself and other people
- listening to other people's points of view
- showing understanding of other people's situations
- expressing your ideas clearly and not at the expense of others
- being able to reach workable solutions to difficulties
- making decisions – even if your decision is to not make a decision!
- being clear about your point and not being sidetracked
- dealing with conflict
- having self-respect and respect for other people
- being equal with others whilst retaining your uniqueness
- expressing feelings honestly and with care

How often are you truly assertive by these standards? Most people find they can be assertive in some types of situations but tend towards aggressive or passive behaviour in others..

Think about situations at home and at work and judge for yourself where your behaviour tends to be on the assertiveness spectrum.

Using the chart on the next page mark where you are now and then put an arrow to where you would like to be in the future.

Add any other general situations in which you know you are not as assertive as you would like to be.

BEHAVIOUR	Passive	Assertive	Aggressive
At home			
At work			
With friends			
In shops			
At the doctor's			

If people say that you are very assertive it probably means that you are generally tending to be aggressive and they are too polite or behaving too passively to tell you the truth!

Fight/flight syndrome

The fight/flight syndrome may explain your response to difficult situations.

Our bodies have evolved to help us deal with physical danger when we are faced with a difficult situation. They instinctively respond by putting us into a physically alert state (i.e. heart pounding, adrenaline flowing) which enables us to either fight the danger or run away.

Despite changes in society our instinctive physical response to difficult situations is still either to fight (aggressive behaviour) or run away (passive behaviour).

Remember that the root cause of aggressive and passive behaviour is fear or lack of self-confidence. Most of us are capable of swinging dramatically from one end of the scale to the other, for seemingly trivial reasons.

While fighting and running away may have been good tactics in the Stone Age they aren't necessarily the most effective way to deal with situations in the 21st Century. However, this does explain why people don't seem to need courses on aggressive or passive behaviour – it just comes naturally!

However, recent research shows that women's behaviour in the face of stress or perceived threat leans towards 'tend and befriend' instead of flight or flight. So they will strengthen social ties, take care of their environment and protect vulnerable people. This behaviour is less apparent in men.

Throughout this workbook we use this definition of assertiveness:

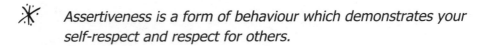

Assertiveness is a form of behaviour which demonstrates your self-respect and respect for others.

Assertiveness is also concerned with dealing with your own feelings about yourself and other people, as much as with the end result.

If your self-respect isn't very high then it may be difficult for you to assert yourself at the moment and your behaviour will tend to be passive; conversely, if you tend not to respect others you will tend towards aggressive behaviour. Only you can truly decide what is assertive for you because only you know what you are thinking and feeling inside.

Assertiveness is about dealing with your feelings.

Assertiveness in practice

Does assertiveness always work? It depends on your objectives. It doesn't guarantee a particular outcome but if the process is followed it usually makes you feel that speaking up for yourself and expressing your feelings is worthwhile.

> Your boss asks you to stay late to finish a piece of work and you are perfectly assertive in your refusal to stay. Your boss isn't in the least impressed and won't reconsider, despite your explanation. Ultimately, she insists and, unless you feel like resigning over it, you realise that you will have to stay late. Your assertiveness hasn't affected the outcome – you still stay late.

However, behaving assertively in that situation has helped in a number of ways:
- You preserve your self-esteem: 'At least I said what I felt and explained properly without getting upset.'
- No one can ever say that you meekly agreed: 'You never said anything last time.'
- You may have provoked your boss into re-assessing you: 'I didn't realise she felt so strongly about that; she's got more to her than I thought.'

Assertiveness may not always be practical if the other person is being very unreasonable or showing erratic behaviour, e.g. dealing with a drunk.

It also may not be appropriate, or even permissible, in very formal situations such as legal disputes where there are rules about what you can and cannot say. However, these are exceptional circumstances.

For the rest of this chapter and the next you will be looking at developing your assertive behaviour in a way that feels appropriate to you. It doesn't mean turning shy people into raving extroverts and it doesn't mean turning zany, fun people into boring grey clones.

Your assertiveness agenda

The exercises that follow are to enable you to be really specific about your agenda for assertiveness.

Write down the real situations that you encounter, either at work or at home, where you would like to be more assertive. Start off with one that isn't very challenging at all. You could probably deal with it if you just got on with it:

Go to the other extreme, and think of the most difficult or frightening situation that you encounter, or that you are avoiding, where you would like to be more assertive. It may be something that makes you feel quite ill to think about, and you may think that nothing can be done about it. Write it down, all the same:

Specific situations

In the next exercise you will be asked to write down more specific situations in which you want to become more assertive. Here are some examples of the types of situations other women have chosen to work on. They are not in any order of difficulty because what may be easy for one woman may be the most difficult for another, and the other way round. They are given purely as prompts to help you think of your own situations. Cover them up if you don't want to be prompted.

Personal

- dealing with comments about living alone
- stopping unwanted emails, texts or social media messages
- stopping my elderly mother from going out half-dressed
- telling my friend I only want her to stay for a week and not blaming anyone else for asking her to go
- asking my family to tidy up after themselves without nagging or getting angry
- dealing with a racist comment on the bus
- getting the children to settle for clothes that aren't 'designer'
- putting my needs first for once
- getting my mortgage/overdraft increased
- telling my partner how I feel about their abusiveness
- having some time to myself each day/week
- talking to my landlord about getting repairs done

Work

- working hours interfering with home life
- saying no to requests for help when I'm overloaded
- colleagues not taking turns to make tea
- refusing to help out Chantal again with her schedules
- speaking up at meetings and/or my appraisal
- standing up for what I believe in with more senior people
- persuading my boss to let me do some of their work
- dealing with a colleague who I know is lying to me
- being sexually or racially harassed at work
- being asked at an interview why I should get the job

YOUR ASSERTIVENESS AGENDA

On page 162 you wrote down an easy and a very difficult situation in which you want to be more assertive.

Now copy the easy one into No. 1 and the difficult one at No. 10 on the list below. Think of other situations to add. Make the low numbers the easier situations and the high numbers the more difficult ones.

Think of as many different situations as you can. Try to get a mixture of: home/work, friends/relatives, big/little, short-term/long-term situations – use the prompt sheet on the previous page if you need more ideas.

Next to each one write down how you deal with them now (passively, aggressively, indirectly aggressively).

1.

2.

3.

4.

5.

6.

7.

8.

9.

10.

 Assertiveness enables each of us to be more ourselves.

Building up notches

Every time you ignore a situation or choose not to deal with it and feel bad about it, it builds up a 'notch' of anger and resentment inside. Eventually, you can get to the point where you blow up.

Ever had days when everything seems to go wrong? Amal copes with this by keeping her head down and keeping out of everyone's way. She may have days, months or even years like this, going home with resentment and frustration, until something snaps. She then swings into her aggressive mode. She may lose her temper over something quite trivial, and everyone is astounded, because she's never said anything before!

How do you feel immediately after you blow up?

And how do you feel a bit later?

Most people feel great at the time and then guilty or ashamed soon after. The danger is that if you feel so guilty later that you feel bad about yourself, you may decide to keep quiet, and build up more notches; you then find yourself in a vicious circle of passive and aggressive behaviour.

Don't forget you can allow yourself NOT to be assertive too! If you know you can choose to be assertive, you can equally choose NOT to assert yourself on any occasion. You may just not feel up to it that day, or you may decide it's not appropriate. You may still choose sometimes to be aggressive or passive because it seems the best short-term solution, but generally these behaviours won't build good long-term relationships.

165

How to be assertive

There are no set phrases, trick techniques or magic words in assertiveness. There are five vital ingredients in any assertive process.

> 1. Listen
>
> 2. Demonstrate understanding
>
> 3. Say what you think and feel
>
> 4. Say specifically what you want to happen
>
> 5. Work out joint solutions

How are you doing?

If you're still not sure whether you're behaving assertively or not, check your feelings about yourself and the other person. Remember that assertiveness is about feeling good about yourself. A useful shorthand way of looking at this is as follows:

ASSERTIVE	AGGRESSIVE
I'm OK	I'm OK
You're OK	You're not OK

PASSIVE	DEPRESSIVE
I'm not OK	I'm not OK
You're OK	You're not OK

Adapted from
I'm OK, You're OK
by Thomas Harris
(Pan)

How to get better at the ingredients

Being more assertive means getting better at all the ingredients and being able to move from one to the other as needed in a conversation. Here are a few hints and tips to polish up each ingredient:

1 Listen

People who are successful at being assertive are good listeners. You may be able to listen well in some circumstances but listening gets more difficult the more complex or controversial the subject matter is. Assertiveness is often about ironing out tricky situations, so listening is a key skill.

Listening is the first key ingredient in an assertive conversation. There is little hope of starting your part of the conversation by demonstrating your understanding if you haven't really taken in what is being said.

It is very difficult to listen to everything that someone is saying, particularly if:

- the other person is waffling or difficult to understand
- you disagree with it
- the other person is expressing very strong feelings
- you experience the other's behaviour as aggressive
- there are distractions
- your mind wanders to other things
- you feel frightened or intimidated
- you are busy thinking about what you are going to say

Mostly, we can spot when someone isn't listening to us.

What are the signs that you notice when someone switches off?

How do you feel when you're not being listened to?

Not being listened to tends to create negative feelings. Keep your listening active to stop these feelings building up in the other person.

People can usually spot if you are not listening to them.

Active listening

Listening well to someone takes a special active effort. It involves:

- quietening yourself down inside
- keeping distractions to a minimum
- paying attention even when you disagree or have strong feelings
- asking questions for clarification
- being open to hear the other person's thoughts, ideas, feelings and intentions
- demonstrating, as well as saying, that you have understood
- giving someone else the space to speak
- being objective about dealing with what you hear

Practise active listening.

2 Demonstrate understanding

Have you experienced someone saying to you, 'I understand how you feel; however ...' and you are quite certain they **don't** understand? True assertiveness is not a set of trick phrases! In true assertiveness you need to demonstrate, by how you listen and by what you say, that you really have understood.

Put yourself in the other person's shoes and then summarise by telling them what you think you heard; how you think they are feeling, what you think they are thinking or what it is that you think they want to do next. This gives them the opportunity to correct you if you are close, but not close enough, in your assessment.

Or you can relate to a similar situation you have faced.

Cassia:

I had been unable to work for over two years because of a real crisis in my health when in the post one day Vikki sent me this quote and said she thought of me when she saw it.

'A long time ago, before I began my search for ways to feel better about myself, I was in a very low state. I was in the middle of a severe personal trauma and I had no self-belief. In fact I had no belief in anything. When we are in the depths of despair and suffer from low self-esteem we lose all sense of trust in ourselves and in other people, and so we feel lonely, vulnerable and afraid. This feeling of vulnerability can make us feel exposed and unprotected and very sensitive to others.'

Then I knew that she really understood how I was.

3 Say what you think and feel

Know what you think and identify your feelings, then make choices about how you communicate your thoughts and feelings.

Different cultures have different ways of communicating and even within the UK culture there is a spectrum of difference. Think back to your upbringing and the family or people that surrounded you then. How did they communicate? Was it thoughts only and not feelings? Was it through direct communication, e.g. 'I feel really angry when you keep ignoring me,' or indirect, e.g. 'You don't seem interested in what I am saying.'

Some families, or if you were looked after, carers or care agencies have a culture of never saying what they feel to each other and so your anger, hurt, guilt and sadness can go on for years without anyone ever really being clear about how you feel. Equally you may shout, scream, bang doors and throw a tantrum but still be leaving the other person to guess what it is that you are really feeling. How do they know whether your banging the door is a result of hurt, anger or whatever? If there is no direct communication of the feelings, the other person is left to guess or has to check what you are feeling by demonstrating that they understand. Indirect communication needs to be followed up with more conversation to reach a point where you can both be sure that you understand.

When you say what you think and feel, be sure to separate the behaviour from the person. This makes it possible for the person to listen to you, because the feedback they are getting is about something they can change.

4 Say specifically what you want to happen

Dropping hints doesn't always work! Being clear about what you want to happen increases the possibility of getting it and minimises the chances of being misunderstood. Of course it doesn't guarantee that you get what you want; you have to be prepared for the other person to say no or have a different point of view. Listen to the response you get.

Make sure you are asking for a change in behaviour, not making a judgement about the person's character or personality.

Judge the circumstances around your request. Have an eye on your long-term goal. If you ask for your maximum then you have room to negotiate and reach a long-term solution.

5 Work out joint solutions and the consequences

Where there is a gap between what you want and what others want, you need to work out a joint solution. A joint solution means joint problem-solving to reach a solution that pleases all parties, not a compromise. Compromise means that neither of you gets what you want. In exploring joint solutions consider the consequences of each choice on yourself and the others concerned.

This is where the real understanding and negotiation starts. You only get to this stage if you have not reached agreement by using the other ingredients. All the other four ingredients need to be used time and time again to arrive at a point where you can either see the other person's point of view or they can see yours and one of you changes your point of view on what you want. If this doesn't happen then you have to agree that you cannot agree.

That's the theory and to put it into practice begin with finding the right words.

Finding the right words

Assertive behaviour involves demonstrating understanding, saying what you think and feel, saying specifically what you want to happen and working out joint solutions. This means finding the right words.

There is masses of research on language that shows the differences in how men and women communicate and how different parts of the UK, different countries and even different age groups can use words differently. See the booklist in Chapter 14.

The use of words gives clues about the behaviour.

You are having trouble getting started on a piece of work which is usually routine. You say to a passing colleague:

Passive: 'Silly me, I'm getting nowhere with this. My brain must be going.'

Aggressive: 'I don't know whose stupid idea it was to say this had to be done this way. I always said this company was run by idiots!'

Assertive: 'Tara, I'm feeling really stuck on this and could do with some help. I know you're too busy right now. When can you spare me 10 minutes later today?'

So let's concentrate on the assertive words!

Using words assertively – beginnings

Very often you have to initiate a conversation. In these cases, you can't initially listen, as nothing has been said! Your opening remarks still need to:

- demonstrate that you understand
- say what you think and feel
- say specifically what you want to happen

Write down an assertive approach to these situations:

You regularly come up with good information for your boss's boss. Your boss has just copied your list into their email and pretended it is their own work. You're very upset about this. You say to your boss:

A colleague has volunteered your help on a project that is behind schedule. You are already very busy and are furious that they should assume you have the time. You say to your colleague:

Your partner/friend messages you so frequently you find it excessive and distracting. You say to them:

Now try one of your own situations from page 164 here.
Your situation:

Your beginning:

Using words assertively – replying

On other occasions you have to respond to someone else. You will need to listen and then:

- demonstrate that you understand
- say what you think and feel
- say specifically what you want to happen

Using the ingredients, write down an assertive response to these scenarios:

You are with a friend booking cinema tickets online for a night out together. You click the wrong button and end up booking for the wrong day. Your friend loses their temper and starts swearing at you and blaming you for other things that have gone wrong with nights out in the past. You say to your friend:

You are keen to take on a new project that will widen your experience and involve you working outside your normal hours. Although you have volunteered for the work, your manager says: 'Well of course you won't be able to cope with this because you'll never be able to juggle the rest of your life to fit around the work.' You reply:

You are applying for a new role for which you have the right experience and qualifications. It's three grades above your current role and you ask your manager to support your application. They laugh and say, 'What on earth are you doing applying for that?' You reply:

Try to avoid using set phrases. Build up some new choices for assertive replies to situations that bother you. Try out one of your own situations from page 164.
Your situation:

Your reply:

Tone of voice and body language

Assertive words need to be matched by the tone of voice and body language. The communication researcher Professor Albert Mehrabian discovered that the overall message that people receive during communication with others is made up of these ingredients:

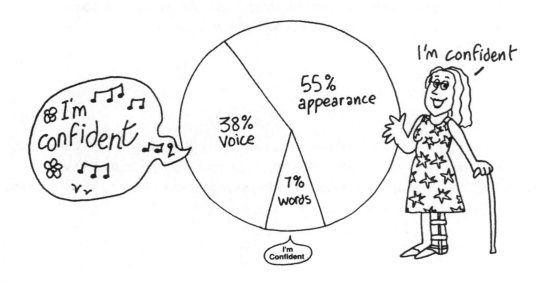

His research was mainly around situations where communication was ambiguous: where the words spoken are inconsistent with the tone of voice or body language of the speaker. If you are surprised or unconvinced by these statistics, consider the huge number of ways you can convey different meanings with a single word, such as 'really', just by changing the volume, pitch, speed and emphasis of your voice. So it is hardly surprising that the voice itself is more than five times more important than the words being spoken. For example: sarcasm only works if the message sent out by the voice and body overrule the actual words being said.

Words, voice and appearance need to deliver the same message. So it's vital to match the body language and tone with the verbal message.

Think about what you hear around you and compile your own examples of aggressive, passive and assertive uses of voice:

Aggressive   **Assertive**   **Passive**

If someone is talking with you on the phone, they will have to base their judgement of your message purely on your words and voice. If they receive an email they have only words and the layout of the message to go on, e.g. using bold or capitals, which equates to shouting. Emojis don't replace body language ☺

Body language varies from country to country, depending on the culture, so it has to be read in conjunction with the other signals. It is dangerous to make judgements from one gesture alone. For example, folding arms may be seen as a shutting off, aggressive gesture. It may also be that the person is cold!

We are all experts in body language. Consciously and unconsciously we read it all day. We know when someone is putting out a mixed message, when the words don't agree with the body language.

OBSERVE – How people sit in the bus, in waiting rooms, at work, and speculate on what you would read from their posture.

TRY OUT – The next time you are with a group of people, sit in a way that you think is assertive for a while – see how it feels and if it matches your words.

Body space

Another aspect of body language concerns the space we give ourselves and others.

Imagine you are travelling home late at night on a train. You are the only person in the carriage until one other passenger boards and sits right next to you, without saying a word or being threatening in any way. How do you feel?

Most of us feel extremely nervous and frightened in that situation. The stranger has become aggressive simply by invading our own personal space.

In day-to-day terms we feel comfortable with some people really close to us and with others we would rather they kept their distance. In his book *Body Language,* Allan Pease describes these spaces as zones. These zones are 'portable air bubbles' that we each have around us.

Zone distances

The sizes of the zones are determined by the culture we've grown up in. For example, while some people are comfortable with crowding, other people are used to wide open spaces and prefer to keep their distance.

The radius of the air bubble around us can be broken down into four distinct zone distances:

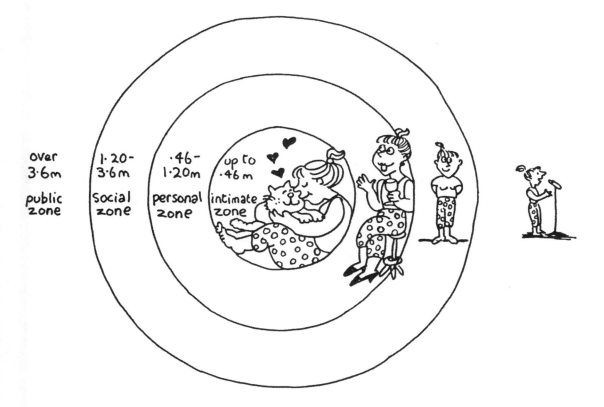

These zone distances tend to apply to people brought up in Australia, New Zealand, the UK and North America.

Intimate Zone 15–45cm (6–18in)

Of all the zone distances this is by far the most important, as it is this zone that a person guards as if it were their own property. Only those who are emotionally close to that person are permitted to enter it. This includes lovers, parents, partner, children, close friends and relatives. There is also a sub-zone that extends up to 15 centimetres (6 inches) from the body which implies physical contact. This is the close intimate zone.

Personal Zone 46cm–1.22m (18–48in)

This is the distance that we stand from others at parties, social functions and friendly gatherings.

Social Zone 1.22–3.6m (4–12ft)

We stand at this distance from strangers, the plumber or carpenter doing repairs, the courier, the shop assistant, new people at work and others we don't know very well.

Public Zone over 3.6m (12ft)

Whenever we address a large group of people, this is the comfortable distance at which we choose to stand.

Being aware of the zones doesn't mean moving around with a tape measure in your hand, but simply being aware of the effect of distance.

You may feel that some people stand too close to you – or don't come close enough! You may have found yourself edging down the corridor because the person you are talking to keeps coming too close, or going up close to some people and seeing them backing off.

People coming too close to you or touching you in an unwelcome way may constitute harassment. Find out about your employer's bullying and harassment policy and decide what you want to do about it.

If you wish people to react to you in a friendly, open way, then be sensitive to the possibility of invading their space – your behaviour may be perceived as aggressive and threatening.

OBSERVE – How close do you stand to other people? Is it comfortable for you? How do you think it is for them? Make notes here about any changes you would like to make:

> *Interesting how easily men own the space around them, while women just feel like visitors without a permit.*
>
> Sarah Dunant – *Fatlands*

MEDITATION – VISUALISE THE GAP

Follow your usual process of relaxing and allowing yourself to let go of today's tensions.

Now bring to mind a person with whom you have an issue and wish to assert yourself. Imagine that person listening to you as you explain your thoughts, feelings and wishes on the issue. Notice what they reply and, for the moment, do not attempt to take the issue forward to resolution; simply allow yourself to be there quietly with your perception and theirs.

Stay with both positions and imagine, on a scale of 10 parts, how far apart you seem to be on the issue. Pay attention to the scale and then experience the points where each of you are now moving closer together.

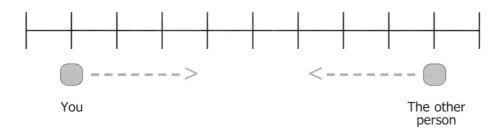

You   The other
                                       person

Return to the present time, open your eyes and focus on whatever is straight ahead of you for a few seconds, to bring yourself back into the room.

179

HAVE A GO!

Turn back to page 164 and your own list of real situations.

Have a go at using assertiveness. Start by tackling your No. 1. If there isn't an appropriate moment for it then pick any of your lower numbered situations – start small:

- have a go at something that doesn't matter too much to you
- recap the main points on page 166 and see how you get on
- review your use of the five ingredients
- record what happens below:

Situation:

I intended to:

What actually happened was:

Looking back, one thing I would do differently is:

Looking back, one thing I'm proud of is:

My feelings about the way I handled it are:

OPTIONAL ACTIVITY – PRACTISE WITH FRIENDS OR COLLEAGUES

One way to build up your skills is to practise with other people who are familiar with this way of working with assertiveness. Team up with someone who is willing to work with the five ingredients, practise as if you are in the situations and give each other feedback.

Summary and action

In this chapter, you have clarified the definition and learned the ingredients of assertiveness. You have practised some assertive responses and beginnings to situations. You have also prioritised situations in which you wish to be more assertive.

Further optional reading

Anne Dickinson – *A Woman in Your Own Right* (Quartet Books)
Dannie Lu Carr – *Brilliant Assertiveness* (Pearson)
Pat Scudamore and Hilton Catt – *Teach Yourself Assertiveness* (Hodder)

Action

What actions will you take now to be more assertive?

- learn the five ingredients of assertiveness at the weekend
- say no next time my manager asks me to do overtime at the weekend
- ask Lynda after the team meeting how she thinks I came across on the assertiveness scale
- at the end of the week record in my journal how much progress I made being assertive
- tonight decide which assertiveness issue I will deal with and then prepare the words with help from Ffion on Thursday

Write yours here:

Specific action   **By when?**

Profile *Dr Anjana Khatwa Ford*

Job Title: Programme Manager for Learning
Organisation: Jurassic Coast Trust

As a young girl growing up in a traditional Asian family, I was aware that women carried the burden of the honour of the family. When the time came, my sister and I would follow in the footsteps of others; an arranged marriage, settling down to a life of compliant domesticity. However, in my heart there burned a yearning for a different pathway; of a career in science. Home was an extremely volatile environment where subjugation, physical violence and emotional degradation of children and women were commonplace.

To survive, I buried myself in school-work and, inspired by my teacher, excelled in Physical Geography. My sister and I wanted to study at university but met with great opposition from the family. I went ahead and gained a degree in Earth Science, but when I was accepted for a PhD in Glacial Geology, my family relationships started to deteriorate. To complicate matters further, I had also fallen in love with a (White) man who I had met on my course. My family said, 'What man will marry a woman with a PhD who is cleverer than he is?'

Misogyny only makes me stronger, but as I started my PhD life at home was getting progressively unbearable. My sister and I left home, making the heart-breaking decision to abandon my brother and mother. Even today, years later, I struggle to cope with the emotion associated with that decision. I had to break the cycle of oppression to achieve my ambitions. Freedom came at a cost, though; we had to apply for a restraining order, were ostracised from the entire family and I was homeless until the University found me accommodation.

After my PhD I worked as an academic in the USA for four years, teaching and researching at different universities. My boyfriend eventually joined me there and gave me unwavering support. I returned to the UK as the new Education Coordinator for the Jurassic Coast, and together we decided to reconnect with my mother. I can't describe the love I felt for her after years of separation and the rift with my family began to heal.

I later married with the full support of my family. Our happy marriage was punctuated by travelling, exciting careers and renovating our Victorian house. I had reached a satisfying point in my career and decided to try for a baby. After a devastating miscarriage, I eventually had a baby girl. However, my husband, who had been cautious about becoming a father, began to experience severe symptoms of post-natal depression. I came home one day to find his belongings gone. He texted to say he'd left and wasn't coming back. My one true friend and soulmate of 15 years was gone and our daughter was only seven months old. I spent three years waiting for his return, raising my daughter as a single mother, managing my career and our home. Perhaps it was misguided but I genuinely believed that his depression would ease and he would return home to us. It was after a life changing trip to Thailand when my daughter was three years old that I realised I could survive and be a parent without him and I started divorce proceedings.

I attribute my survival during this period mainly to my mother, who called every single day with messages of love and support. A Children's Centre case worker and my friends provided me with advice and the respite I needed from the exhaustion and loneliness of being a lone parent. Counselling also gave me the confidence to move on with my life. Now I have an amazing partner of three years (whom I met online!), we have a blended family with our amazing three children, my career is back on track and I ran my first half marathon this year!

When I reflect back on my story, I realise that I am a fighter and a survivor. If you see me standing outside the school gates, you'd never know about the barriers I broke down and the conventions I challenged. That gives me an immense sense of pride and power.

Learning points

- Strive for what you believe in. This is the true path to happiness and fulfilment, even though the journey may be rocky and uncomfortable.
- You never know what significant barriers you are capable of overcoming until you try.
- However difficult life may seem, when you look back you'll see strengths that you didn't know you had until then.
- In times of crisis you will find the support you need, or it will find you.

8

> *It took me quite a long time to develop a voice, and now that I have it, I am not going to be silent.*

Madeleine Albright

Using Assertiveness Positively

Objective
- to put assertiveness skills into practice to help you achieve your goals

This chapter is important because

- assertiveness is easy in theory, but difficult in practice
- the basic ingredients can be adapted to fit different circumstances

Contents
- practising assertiveness
- using assertiveness when you:
  - are asked for straight information
  - find inconsistency in someone's behaviour
  - need a response from someone
  - aren't being listened to, or aren't being taken notice of
  - are dealing with someone's strong feelings
  - have strong feelings yourself
  - want to say 'no'
  - give and receive criticism
  - give or receive a compliment
- being assertive with yourself
- summary and action
- profile of Sarah Harvey

Practising assertiveness

In this chapter you have the opportunity to see how you can find the words to be assertive in a wide range of different situations.

Using assertiveness when you are asked for straight information

It hardly seems necessary to learn assertiveness in order to reply to a straight question, but many people tie themselves in verbal knots to avoid giving straight answers to straight questions.

For example

'What time is the meeting on Tuesday?'

Passive: 'Umm – I think it might be 3 o'clock, but then I'm not sure. You'd better check with someone else. Sorry.'
Aggressive: 'You mean you don't know? You were there when it was organised. Why don't you get yourself together?'
Assertive: '3 o'clock.'

YOUR ASSERTIVE REPLIES

Write down your assertive reply to these questions:

'Who's going to make the tea?'

'When will you have that report ready for me?'

'How do you feel about this Springboard workbook right now?'

Using assertiveness when you find inconsistency in someone's behaviour

An inconsistency may be:
- when someone says one thing and does another
- when someone contradicts something they've already said
- when the printed policy says one thing and the accepted practice is another
- when someone says one thing and looks as if they mean another

The assertive response is not to demand that everything is consistent in life, but to:
- point out the inconsistency
- express the effect of the inconsistency on you
- say what you want to happen

For example

'You said I didn't have enough experience so I didn't apply for that job. Now it's been given to someone with less experience than me. I'm now confused and annoyed about this, and I would like an explanation.'

YOUR ASSERTIVE RESPONSE

Write an assertive response to these inconsistencies:

Your partner has been extremely supportive of you and your career, but has recently started making sarcastic remarks when you work on the revision for your exams.

At your manager's suggestion, you have organised a day out to visit other parts of your current organisation and are keen to go. Your manager now says you can't go because of work pressure.

Using assertiveness when you need a response from someone

When someone uses passive behaviour, it can be difficult to discover what their thoughts and feelings are. They may not know what they are or have decided it is not relevant or appropriate, or be too scared to express them.

Alternatively, someone may be indirectly aggressive and be choosing not to speak. You may prefer them to voice their opinion on a subject at the time, so you know where you stand and can avoid them saying afterwards: 'Well of course, I never actually agreed with that decision.'

The assertive approach is to make very specific requests to individuals.

For example

'Well, we've aired the subject of the new computer system at length. I'm pretty clear about where Usha, Tim and Gilli stand. Wyn, I'd like to hear your views on this.'

YOUR ASSERTIVE RESPONSE

Write down how you would find out:

How your partner feels about going to your family again for Christmas, Divali, Eid or some other special time.

What's wrong with a friend who seems to have avoided you since you were promoted to a grade higher?

Using assertiveness when you aren't being listened to or aren't being taken notice of

When you suspect you aren't being listened to, the tendency is to move towards either aggressive or passive behaviour. An assertive way of dealing with this is simply to repeat the essential parts of your message, while continuing to acknowledge the other person.

For example

Your manager and you are about to go to a meeting and they are hassling you to get to the meeting on time.

Manager: 'Come on, we'll be late for the meeting.'
You: 'We've got 10 minutes yet, I'll be ready.'
Manager: 'We'd better get going now.'
You: 'I'll be ready within 10 minutes.'

MAKING SURE YOU'RE HEARD

Work out an assertive way of ensuring that you are heard in these situations:

You are at a meeting where it is assumed that you will stay until 5 pm. You need to leave at 4 pm to collect your children from the childminder.

You are explaining to your friend that you do not want her to assume that you will always go out with her on Thursday nights.

> ❝ *I raise up my voice, not so I can shout, but so those without a voice can be heard; we cannot succeed when half of us are held back.* ❞
>
> Malala Yousafzai

189

Using assertiveness when you are dealing with someone's strong feelings

One of the vital ingredients in assertiveness is to demonstrate your understanding of the other person. When you think that a situation is particularly sensitive, and feelings are running strongly, it is even more important to demonstrate your understanding. This doesn't mean you have to agree with the other person, but demonstrating your understanding keeps communication going.

Anger is for many the most difficult emotion to deal with. When people are very angry they often don't say 'I'm very angry' or 'I'm furious', but it is obvious from their tone and appearance. Acknowledging the feeling often defuses the situation.

For example

You think your mother is angry about something because she keeps snapping at you.

You: 'You seem angry or upset. What's the matter?'

YOUR ASSERTIVE RESPONSE

Write down your assertive response to these situations:
A colleague has just returned to work after having arranged her father's funeral. Acknowledge what's happened:

A neighbour shouts at you because they think you were playing loud music late at night and kept them awake. It wasn't you. Acknowledge their feelings and resolve the situation:

Using assertiveness when you have strong feelings yourself

It isn't always possible to think of something positive to say in every situation. Sometimes all you're left with are negative feelings and wishing things were different. In these circumstances, say so. It is important to:

- be very specific
- describe the behaviour that you find upsetting, rather than having a go at the person
- say how this affects you
- say what you would like to happen next

For example

'When you drive this close to the car in front, I feel very nervous. Could you leave a bit more space?'

EXPRESS YOUR FEELINGS ASSERTIVELY

Write down your response, saying how you feel and what you would like to happen:

Your friend is flicking through magazines and saying 'mmmm' while you're trying to say something really important to her.

You have been working very hard to organise a staff meeting on childcare facilities, which you are very keen to attend. Your boss now tells you that she thinks there is no reason for you to attend the meeting and wants you to answer the phones while everyone else goes.

191

Using assertiveness when you want to say 'no'

'No' is one of the shortest but most difficult words for most of us to say.

Write down why you have difficulty saying 'no':

No wonder saying 'yes' is easier, even when you'd prefer to say 'no'!

Assertive behaviour means saying 'no' and backing it up with an explanation if you wish. It does not mean making excuses or apologies or justifying yourself, i.e. going on and on giving excuses (sometimes not even true ones!) so that the other person will think well of you or at least think your reasons are good enough.

For example

'Could you give me a lift to the station?'

Passive: 'I'm sorry – I can't. I would if I could, but tonight I've got to be at the other end of town to pick my sister up, and the traffic might be bad and I don't want to upset her by being late again. I'm ever so sorry.'

Aggressive: 'Not likely. No way. Why should I?'

Assertive: 'No' plus an assertive explanation if you wish, e.g. 'No, I'm picking my sister up tonight.'

OBSERVE HOW PEOPLE SAY 'NO'

Over the next two days listen to yourself and other people saying 'no' and make notes on how people do it well.

Using assertiveness when you need to give criticism

As with saying 'no', many people avoid criticism, as it can be uncomfortable and negative. Giving criticism assertively gives opportunities for change to happen, and often clears the air.

There are five steps in giving criticism assertively:

1. Give specific examples of the behaviour you're criticising

2. Say how you feel about the effect it has on you

3. Say what changes you'd prefer to see

4. Listen to the response (words, voice and body language)

5. Work out a joint solution (not a compromise) to take you into the future – don't get bogged down in what has happened

For example

You overhear a colleague making a sarcastic remark about another colleague.

You: 'When you talk about about Isabelle like that I feel really angry. I don't like the implication that she's big-headed and superior and I'd rather you spoke about her more sensitively.'

GIVE SOME CRITICISM

Think of a real situation where you would like to give criticism in order to bring about a change. Write it down, then try it out:

Using assertiveness when you need to receive criticism

Remaining open to receiving criticism takes courage. It is one of the ways you have of finding out the effect you have on other people and enables you to decide whether you want to change your behaviour or not. Do not fall into the trap of feeling you have to justify yourself.

There are four steps:

Remain open – listen to what is being said and ask for specific examples to clarify your own understanding

Let the other person know you've heard and understood the criticism, by giving the other person your immediate response

Take time to decide: is it all true, is it partly true, is it totally false, what do you want to do?

Change your behaviour if you want to

For example

'I can see that my not speaking up at meetings could be interpreted as my not being interested. I'm not sure how I feel about that at the moment, or what I might choose to do differently and will give it some thought.'

PRACTISE 'CRITICISM SITUATIONS'

If you are working through this workbook with other women, get together with two of them to practise giving and receiving criticism, and to do the exercise on the next page. If you are working through it on your own, see who among your family/friends/colleagues will be prepared to read the sections on assertiveness and join you in practising:

1. *Person One describes the situation and the characters briefly and then practices being her best assertive self in that situation.*

2. *Person Two takes the role of the other character, behaving as briefed by Person One.*

3. *If there is a third person, ask them to observe, take notes and give feedback.*

4. *After the practice, participants and observer discuss what they have seen and heard and make constructive suggestions. You may then want to have another go at practising being assertive in the same situation, incorporating the feedback suggestions.*

Practise:
*   *giving criticism*
*   *receiving criticism*
*   *observing and giving feedback*

Make a note of what you learnt, and have a go at compliments. (See below)

 Being open to criticism enables you to grow.

Using assertiveness when you need to give or receive a compliment

We live in a culture where compliments are regarded with great suspicion. Giving them and receiving them is difficult, as people may either think that you're 'crawling' to them or that you have an ulterior motive. Giving and receiving feedback, including compliments, is an important aspect of assertiveness.

Receiving compliments comfortably boosts your self-esteem. People with less self-esteem tend to discount all compliments. Make sure you listen to the ones that come your way. Aim to give out compliments and positive feedback at least 20 times as often as you give criticism or negative feedback.

To give a compliment – keep it short and to the point.

To receive a compliment – keep it short and don't push it away or run yourself down. You may also want to say how you feel.

For example

Receiving a compliment:
'You made a really good job of that piece of work.'

Passive: 'Oh it wasn't particularly difficult – Bryn did most of it anyway.'
Aggressive: (sarcastic) 'Oh you noticed, did you?'
Assertive: 'Thanks. I was pleased with it too.'

GIVING AND RECEIVING REAL COMPLIMENTS

Practise giving and receiving compliments with two friends or colleagues:
- *Person One gives a real compliment to*
- *Person Two, who listens, stays open minded and accepts it, while*
- *Person Three observes how the other two get on, then gives feedback*

Then swap roles until everyone has had two turns in each role.

YOUR AGENDA FOR ASSERTIVE ACTION

Write down some situations in which you want to be more assertive. Choose whichever of the following categories are relevant to you:

Giving straight information

Inconsistency in someone's behaviour

Getting a response from someone

When you aren't being listened to or being taken notice of

When you are dealing with other people's strong feelings

When you have strong feelings yourself

When you want to say 'no'

When you need to give criticism

When you need to receive criticism

When you need to give or receive a compliment

Tackle three of these over the next two weeks.

197

MEDITATION

Imagining having a positive influence in the world can help you feel stronger and more confident. Close your eyes, relax your body and breathe easily and slowly. Imagine that as you breathe in you are breathing in a fine mist of a colour that you need right now to strengthen you. Choose any colour that you wish and allow the colour to change if you want it to. Use colour in a way that helps you, even if the colour generally has other meanings, e.g. blue – calm and restful, yellow – lightness and energy. You may not find blue restful, so decide your own meaning. Spend two to five minutes concentrating on this breathing taking in the colour.

Now imagine that as you breathe out you are also able to breathe out a colour that will help a situation that needs to be resolved in the world or in a group or community that you care about. As you breathe out imagine your breath somehow reaching that situation in a positive way. Do this for two to five minutes.

When you notice you are reaching a conclusion round off your meditation by bringing your attention back into the place where you are now, open your eyes and stretch your body.

Being assertive with yourself

Difficulties with assertiveness often start before we open our mouths, as the most challenging relationship to handle is the relationship we have with ourselves. This sets the scene for our relationships with other people.

Being assertive with yourself:
- stops you underrating yourself
- identifies what you really need
- makes you more productive
- lets you know what you're good at
- helps your actions follow your intentions

The conversations we have with ourselves have a huge effect on the outcomes of situations. They usually become self-fulfilling prophecies, so if you're feeling anxious and sceptical about something, it is likely that you will only 'tune in' to those aspects which fit with your anxiety and scepticism.

In the examples that follow, if the unassertive voice is allowed to rule, Tuesday will be a disaster and the meeting with the friend could end with a row. The assertive voice gives a much better chance of success.

UNASSERTIVE VOICE

'It's Tuesday and it's the departmental meeting. That means everyone's going to be in a bloody mood. It also means I'll be given all sorts of stupid things to do. If that Gus asks me for one more special favour I'll scream! I don't know how I'm going to get through the day.'

'I've read all the stuff on assertiveness now, and it seems pretty straightforward. I'll catch Xenia tonight and tell her that I'm not going to her party next week. I'm sure she'll see my point. I'll just give it to her straight.'

ASSERTIVE VOICE

'It's Tuesday and it's the departmental meeting – usually a difficult day. I'll deal with each situation as it crops up and practise remaining calm and assertive. I'll say "no" to Gus if I have no time to do him a favour.'

'I'll be open and honest with Xenia tonight and discuss with her how I feel about her party next week. It won't necessarily be a comfortable conversation but it's important for me to sort it out.'

The final aspect of being assertive with yourself involves believing in your own feelings, and really valuing them. This may mean breaking away from your habitual patterns of behaviour, to really explain what's going on inside yourself and stop making excuses to yourself:

- your assertive self is honest, rational, realistic and consistent
- your assertive self is able to assess your own performance accurately and objectively

- your assertive self encourages you
- your assertive self may get shouted down by the other internal voices

What do the other, non-assertive internal voices say to stop you being assertive with yourself?

For example

Your sympathetic friend: 'Her needs are greater than mine.'

Your critic: 'Is that the best you can do? It's terrible.'

Your mouse: 'They'll misunderstand me – I'll just keep quiet.'

Your perfectionist: 'If you can't do it perfectly, then it's not worth even starting.'

Your moaner: 'What can I do? There's no point. Nobody will listen.'

RESPONDING TO YOUR NON-ASSERTIVE INTERNAL VOICES

Add some of your own and write down what you are going to say to them the next time they speak up:

Voice   **Your positive response**

YOUR ASSERTIVENESS AGENDA

Think of situations in which you are now going to be more assertive with yourself and add them to the ones on pages 164 and 196. You've already practised or dealt with some of them, so tackle another one, and work up to your No. 10. Aim to have dealt with most of them, including No. 10, by the end of the workbook.

Don't worry about getting it perfect. Have a go and assertively review your achievements.

Summary and action

In this chapter you have worked through examples of being assertive in many different situations.

YOUR PERSONAL RESOURCE BANK

On page 284, note the situations in which you now feel you can be truly assertive.

Further optional reading

Ken and Kate Back – *Assertiveness at Work* (McGraw Hill)
Susan Wilson Solovic – *The Girls' Guide to Power and Success* (American Management Association)
Sheryl Sandberg – *Lean In* (W.H. Allen)

Action

What actions will you take now to develop your assertiveness further?

Here are some suggestions:

- next week I'll tackle situation No. 1 on page 164
- at our next Springboard group get together we'll practise assertiveness
- I'll ask HR about an assertiveness workshop on Friday
- tomorrow I'll give five compliments to people at work

Write yours here:

Specific Action   **By When?**

   *Take care of the small steps – the big changes
will then take care of themselves.*

Profile *Sarah Harvey*

*Job Title: Senior Learning and Organisational
         Development Assistant*
Organisation: Dorset County Council

I come from a small, but close family and have one
sister. She's adopted and I'm so lucky to have her!

I was an average student at school – I worked hard but
didn't excel when it came to exams. I did a secretarial course after sixth form,
and started work in a typing bureau in a large organisation, a good grounding.
After 18 months I moved to another organisation as a PA – big mistake! I
wasn't ready, my boss terrified me and I didn't like working alone. I was very
unhappy and I vividly remember my Mum saying, 'You go to work to earn a
living; you don't live to go to work – move on.' I got another job within a
matter of weeks, joined Dorset County Council at the age of 22 and have
remained in local government ever since, mainly in secretarial/administrative
roles within Human Resources.

I've seen a lot of restructures and re-organisations, learning to be resilient and
adaptable with a positive approach to change. Currently nine councils are
merging to form two and I'll take advantage of support such as interview skills
training and wellbeing learning events. I have confidence and belief in my skills
and experience and these will help to secure my future in the new organisation.

I married my husband, Nick, over 20 years ago (it seems a long time now – we
eloped to Gretna Green). We'd already been together for six years, so started a
family straight away. We've been blessed with two wonderful daughters
although it wasn't an easy journey. Although told by a fertility clinic we would
not be able to conceive naturally, we did – eventually! I also suffered a
miscarriage with what would have been our third child. It was very difficult at
the time and I'm now thankful that it didn't happen with my first pregnancy.
After trying to conceive for so long, I think it would have destroyed me.

Our strong relationship, the ability to provide emotional support for each other,
was really important as we coped with the loss of our child. It was physically
traumatic for me; my grief and sense of loss happened immediately. I gave
myself the time and space to grieve for what might have been and was able to

203

reflect and be grateful for the two healthy children we already had. My husband had a tough time some weeks later and I was then more able to support him. Deciding not to have more children helped us restore a sense of control, knowing we wouldn't have to go through this again.

Since having a family, my focus has been on work/life balance. I've always worked: part-time, full-time, term-time, zero-hours, I've tried them all to get the right balance. I've been as flexible I can with the council and it feels like it's worked both ways.

The last few years have been difficult; my Dad, Mum and sister were all diagnosed with cancer within two years of each other. Sadly my Dad lost his fight. I still miss him terribly and think about him every day. Happily my sister is cured and if you take only one thing from my story, please, please don't ever put off having cervical screening – it definitely saved her life. My Mum lives with cancer and receives great care at the Royal Marsden Hospital. During all these ups and downs my family have been my rock. The distractions of work routine and the support of colleagues have prevented me being consumed by the situation.

I've worked in Learning and Organisational Development for two years in a very varied role. There are many opportunities for growth and development; this environment has made me realise, more than ever, the importance of keeping learning and challenging myself personally and professionally. I may be closer to pension than A levels, but with apprenticeships now available to all, that could provide a great opportunity to upskill. Who knows where it might take me!

Learning points

- Believe in yourself and never give up.
- It's all about balance – be the best you can be at work but balance it with the important things in life – which for me are my family and making the most of my lovely Mum.
- Be positive and try to see challenges as opportunities.
- Keep learning and take advantage of opportunities like coaching and mentoring to help you achieve your professional goals.
- Make contacts. Don't do everything by email or instant message. Talk to people, face to face. Those contacts will almost certainly come in handy.

> *Don't underestimate the value of Doing Nothing, of just going along, listening to all the things you can't hear, and Not Bothering.* **,**

Winnie the Pooh

More Energy – Less Anxiety

Objectives
- to recognise your levels of stress and pressure
- to build awareness of unhelpful patterns of thoughts and feelings
- to create new mental habits to deal with stress and overcome pressure
- to find ways to raise your energy level when you need to

This chapter is important because

- your energy needs to be maintained or recharged
- prevention is better than cure
- thinking and feeling can drive behaviour unconsciously

Contents
- healthy pressure levels
- how do you know when you're stressed?
- making a fresh start
- practical approaches
- new responses to old triggers
- summary and action
- profile of Hilary M. Jones

Balancing the conflicting demands of a busy life can be a major headache or dynamic way of living. Our inner environment also places demands upon us, often unconsciously. The key to more energy and less anxiety is achieving balance and dealing with the automatic reactions that may increase the pressure we feel. Each person has to find their own point of balance and the right tools to reach it.

This chapter gives hints and tips for assessing your pressure levels, keeping going, making sure you don't burn out, getting off autopilot to take more control over your mind and remembering to have fun!

Healthy pressure levels

Pressure is healthy as long as you don't overdo it. Where the level of work and activity in your life is about right you will generally feel OK. Distress or, in some cases, disease results when:

- you're unaware of the pressure that your mind and body are under
- you have too much or too little to do
- you feel you have little control over your situation
- what you have to do is too difficult, boring, time-consuming
- you keep going beyond your energy resources
- your unconscious reactions are creating fight/flight energy
- unexpected events and pressure overwhelm you
- you experience unhealthy pressure levels for extended periods

Physical, mental and emotional symptoms creep in unnoticed and can cause illness if the source of the pressure is not addressed. The best way to manage pressure levels is to notice them early.

Experiment now as you read this. Freeze your body in the position it is in right this minute. Notice where the tension is in your body, how much pressure you're putting on any one spot. Let go as much of the tension as you can and balance your body as best you can to reduce pressure or tension on that spot.

When you are under pressure, where do you usually feel tension in your body?

> Hanna:
>
> I knew I was busy; work was just that way – dashing from job to job, keeping all the balls in the air, no down time. Life felt like a game of Jenga; if one piece came out wrong, everything might totter and fall. But I thought I was handling it. It felt edgy, almost like a high.
>
> Then I began to miss deadlines, struggled to get out of bed in the morning, arrived late for meetings and finally (embarrassingly) started bursting into tears for no reason. I realised then it was serious; I had to take better care of myself, reduce my commitments, stop living on energy drinks and chocolate.

What is the stress level in your life now?

over the top, too much pressure ☐
a bit high, some pressure ☐
comfortable, just right pressure ☐
uncomfortable, too little pressure ☐

What causes you stress now?

What are you already doing about it?

What do you foresee that may cause you stress in the near future?

❝ *It's not good to cross the bridge before you get to it.* ❞

Judi Dench

How do you know when you're stressed?

People know they are stressed when they get ill or find themselves in distress, but what about your early warning signals?

Do you experience any of these?

one or two nights of not sleeping well	YES/NO
forgetting things	YES/NO
biting nails, lip or cheek	YES/NO
diarrhoea	YES/NO
wanting more time to yourself	YES/NO
eating too much/too little	YES/NO
excessive worrying	YES/NO
smoking more	YES/NO
drinking more alcohol	YES/NO
taking non-prescription drugs	YES/NO
feeling sick	YES/NO
expecting yourself to do more/better	YES/NO
being irritable	YES/NO
having minor accidents	YES/NO
feeling angry, hurt, worried, unhappy	YES/NO
having aches and pains	YES/NO
feeling tense or anxious	YES/NO
getting breathless on little exertion	YES/NO
high blood pressure	YES/NO
high cholesterol	YES/NO

Add anything of your own that you know or think is a symptom of your being stressed:

How many symptoms are you experiencing now?

What can you find locally? Look at noticeboards or websites: library, community centre, leisure centre or gym, doctor's surgery, health food store, newsagent's window. Where is the nearest park, hypnotherapist, swimming pool, yoga class or reflexologist?

Make use of technology. There are many good apps to help you practise breathing or mindfulness. Apps can monitor and record exercise levels and frequency, happiness scores and stress symptoms. Relaxation and visualisation audio tracks can be streamed or downloaded. Wearable tech can give you real time information on your physiology.

Notice, ask about and explore how people around you cope with, manage or overcome stress and pressure. Ask how they keep going, deal with setbacks or manage when they are overwhelmed by things such as work, events, thoughts or feelings. Be curious to discover their strategies.

The final step is to be assertive with yourself to make sure that you go and do it, whatever 'it' is, and then use the positive nurturing part of yourself to reward yourself for doing it and just keep on doing it if you enjoy it.

Note any strategies you have tried or would like to try:

Practical approaches

There are many techniques and exercises to help you deal with worry, overcome nerves, reduce anxiety and change unhelpful behaviour patterns, thinking and feeling that drain your energy. The rest of this chapter gives some ideas and strategies.

Overcoming everyday nerves

In day-to-day activities people may experience sudden attacks of nerves which can grow into panic or anxiety. Nerves are normal and their effects can be overcome or at least minimised. So if, for example, you find yourself getting nervous before an interview or presentation, or other day-to-day home or work situation, try some of these strategies.

They have cumulative effects. Doing them regularly is like topping up your calmness bank, which you can then draw on in times of need.

The keys to overcoming nerves are:
- breathing
- releasing tension
- preparation and planning

Breathing

Breathing is automatic – thankfully. But it isn't automatically done to the best of your ability. Many people breathe high up in the ribcage and their abdomen doesn't move. This means just a small proportion of air in your lungs exchanges and your body loses out on a richer supply of energy-giving oxygen. To improve your breathing think about it, or work on it, for only a minute or two at a time. Any more and you'll get dizzy! Doing the meditations earlier in the workbook has already built up your experience.

TWO-MINUTE PAUSE

Wherever you are sitting, make yourself upright and comfortable. When you've read all the instructions, begin:

- *note the time*
- *close your eyes or just lower them to the ground if you are somewhere too public*
- *breathe through your nose, concentrating on breathing out extra, pushing the air out with your tummy muscles. This is better for you than taking in a deep breath*
- *let your breathing settle again and repeat the longer out-breath three times*
- *then sit quietly just noticing the breath going in and out over your upper lip until you*

estimate two minutes have passed
- *open your eyes and check the time*

The first time you do this, two minutes may seem a long time, or it may have passed quickly. If you haven't done this kind of exercise before it may seem strange or you may feel self-conscious. Do persevere. Practise pausing regularly and you'll get better and better at it and it will calm you down more effectively.

Enhancing your breathing a few times a day balances out and counteracts the times you hold your breath or breathe too shallowly. You can also use this exercise before interviews or other nerve-wracking events.

Remember – breathe out!

Releasing tension

When people feel nervous they often carry tension in their muscles. This short practice can help to relax your whole body. You can use it to follow on after the two-minute pause on the previous page.

TWO-MINUTE RELEASE

Start as for the two-minute pause then tell each part of your body to release. Say the word 'release' softly or silently. It's gentle. Repeat it slowly and quietly to yourself while you:

- *release your*
    - *head*
    - *face muscles*
    - *jaw and teeth*
- *let your shoulders drop*
- *release your*
    - *neck*
    - *shoulders*

- *arms*
- *chest*
- *tummy*
- *legs*
- *feet*

Go into as much detail as you like. Remember – you may not feel anything happening at first, but keep repeating regularly to build up your experience.

Preparation and planning

Planning substitutes thinking for worrying! Having a plan and being prepared enables you to contain any worrying and to feel more in control. Worry about imminent events, as well as those in the short- and medium-term future, is a major stress factor for many people. As with your goal setting in Chapter 6, you can work out a plan of what you want to achieve and how you will achieve it in any setting. This may lead to a string of thoughts about 'What if ... ?', e.g. What if the train is late? What if they ask me about budgeting? What if she says 'no'? Part of your planning for an event needs to include your 'what if's'.

Think of one event in the future that you are apprehensive about. Pin down one of your 'what if' statements about this event. Then put down every idea you can come up with to deal with it, from the most reasonable to the downright wild!

What if ... ?   **I will ...**

*You're worried about what ifs.
Well, what if you stopped worrying?*

Shannon Celebi – *Driving off Bridges*

Paying attention

Our minds are very often busy, full of thoughts, frequently not about the things we are engaged in at that moment. These thoughts can distract us and, even worse, we evaluate and judge ourselves, ruminate about the past or worry about the future. Noticing these thoughts is the first step to taking more control over our minds, which we'll cover later in this chapter.

Try this two-minute exercise concentrating on a totally unimportant object. It's normal to struggle to keep your focus during this practise. Just notice any thoughts, other than those about the object, allow them to pass like clouds and bring your attention back to the object. Let go of any judgements of how good you are (or should be!) at concentrating on a simple object. By practising regularly every day for a month, you'll find your concentration on more important things improves enormously.

TWO-MINUTE CONCENTRATION

Take a very simple object that comes to hand such as a pen, paper clip or teaspoon and concentrate on it for two minutes. For the two minutes think about as many aspects of the object as possible. For example:

- what it is
- where it came from
- what it looks like
- how it is made
- what it is made of
- what it is used for
- what it could be used for

When you find your mind wandering, bring it back to the object. Don't worry if at first you run out of thoughts before the two minutes are up.

I think self-awareness is probably the most important thing towards being a champion.

Billie Jean King

Building self-awareness

You've been practising concentration and noticing the other thoughts that come into your mind. As far as we know, humans are the only species able to do this. We can be ourselves and at the same time take the position of an observer and notice ourselves being ourselves.

Everyone tends to have patterns of thinking and mostly they are unconscious. Working towards taking more control of your mind means becoming aware of your thoughts.

THOUGHT QUESTIONNAIRE

Whilst you were concentrating on your simple object in the previous exercise you probably had a wide range of thoughts not about that object. Take a moment to record some examples of the type of thoughts you were having. Or if it's a while since you did the exercise write the thoughts that most often distract you or are familiar to you.

Thoughts about:

– the exercise
e.g. Wish I had a more interesting pen. How long has it been now? What's the point of this? I bet everyone else finds this easy.

– yourself
e.g. Am I doing this right? What happens if I fall asleep? I'm so excited today.

– others
e.g. Why is my boss so irritating? My sister is not looking well. Cuddles with my son are always uplifting. Mum really deserves a break. I have a great team at work.

– the past
e.g. Last night was great fun. My partner used to be so supportive. I can't believe I really did that. How did she manage to get that job? Did I lock the front door this morning?

– the future
e.g. Its going to be tough next week. What shall I pack for the weekend? Maybe I will just tell them. She'll come next week. If I win the lottery ... If only ... I wish ... I hope ...

– judging or evaluating yourself and others
e.g. I'll never be good enough to ... She's so brilliant at that. They should let me ... I'm so rubbish at ... It's terrible that ... I'll always be able to ...

– anything else

e.g. any other thoughts that frequently come to mind or patterns of thinking that you notice.

We are much more than our thoughts, although we can act as if we are controlled by them, even when they are unhelpful.

Thoughts are difficult to control or manage.
- they are almost impossible to turn off
- it's hard to replace unwelcome thoughts with different ones
- distracting yourself with other activities doesn't work for long
- working hard to control thoughts uses up energy

This can increase stress and pressure. Being able to notice your thoughts and feelings creates a space, switching off your autopilot. The space allows you to choose to respond more effectively to unhelpful or unwanted, difficult or destructive thoughts and feelings.

A useful approach is to just accept the thought or feeling, allow it to be there and move ahead with what you want to do. So acknowledge nerves before an interview and decide to be your best self at the moment you need to.

How is it for you to just accept thoughts and feelings, not act on them?

New responses to old triggers

It is particularly difficult to accept and move on from negative and unhelpful thoughts and those which are triggered by events or memories. We will work with these now.

If you are attending a Springboard programme work through the visualisation below with a partner. If not find a trusted friend/colleague or partner to do this work with you.

EXPERIENCING A TRIGGER

Care note: In this exercise you'll be asked to think of a situation that triggers difficult feelings or thinking. It's best to avoid working with situations involving significant loss or bereavement until you have more experience with these techniques.

Bring to mind a recent or repeated situation in which you were triggered with unhelpful feelings and/or thinking such as disappointment, sadness, anger, hurt, frustration. Then describe the situation to your partner, speaking uninterrupted for two minutes.

Your partner will help by asking:
- what was the event?
- what were the feelings that arose?
- what was the very first feeling that came?
- where in your body did you feel it/do you feel it now?

Now your partner will read this script to you:

Now you are sitting comfortably in your chair, start by focusing on your breathing. You can close your eyes if that is comfortable for you, to allow you to focus on what is happening inside. Simply breathe normally for the next few breaths (PAUSE ...).

Bring to mind the event you were just talking about in which unpleasant, unhelpful or difficult emotions were triggered. Imagine revisiting that event now in your mind. You are going to practise a response strategy.

Your first step is to just pause and notice you have been triggered. And in that noticing just allow yourself to breathe. The act of noticing provides you the space to breathe more deeply for a 30 second pause. We'll stay in this state of pause for 30 seconds (PAUSE for 30 seconds).

Now just bring your attention to your body to pay attention to the emotion that has arisen. What does that emotion feel like in your body? Where is that emotion in your body? What do you notice about the temperature or tension in maybe your neck, back, shoulders, chest, head or hands? Now just spend a few moments experiencing that emotion as a bodily sensation, without judging it or pushing it away.

It may help to name the emotions, saying to yourself silently, 'I am experiencing anger in my body' or 'I am experiencing frustration in my body'. Now we'll pause for 60 seconds to allow you to just keep experiencing the emotions (PAUSE for 60 seconds).

Now let's investigate. Where has that feeling come from? What is its history? If your trigger involved another person imagine them looking at you. What are they noticing about you? Just spend a short time investigating and reflecting, getting a sense of perspective without judging or evaluating (PAUSE for 30 seconds).

Next let's spend a few moments building your response to the situation or event. Bring to mind how you can respond, with the perspective you have gained, in a way that will lead to a positive outcome. Imagine the most positive and kindest response you can give. What would that sound like, feel like, look like? Just spend a few moments now creating that response in your mind (PAUSE for 30 seconds).

Now that you have imagined your positive response you are going to return to the present. Focus now on your breathing again for the next few moments (PAUSE ...).

Now make a tight fist with one or both hands, holding on to any of that remaining emotion. Now slowly release your fist, allowing the emotion to float away. Just energy joining the energy in the room.

Bring your focus now back to your breathing for the next 30 seconds (PAUSE for 30 seconds).

Now you've completed your response strategy, open your eyes and notice the room and people around you.

Dealing with triggers

The approach to dealing with triggers

1. Notice you have been triggered

2. Pause to breathe

3. Pay attention and experience the feeling

4. Investigate the feeling and gain perspective

5. Build a response for a positive outcome

This technique requires practice and so start with easier situations and move on to more difficult ones. Keep practising. Even if you can manage only one of the ingredients when you are triggered you are still becoming more self-aware.

Defusing thoughts

Sometimes it helps to use techniques to reduce the power of our difficult thoughts. Saying things out loud can help them sound less harmful and can sharpen your observation of the thought or feeling.

CALLING OUT THE THOUGHT

Take a moment now to identify a difficult thought – one that you often experience, perhaps about yourself, the world, other people or the future. It could be a fear, worry, doubt, criticism or regret that has a significant impact upon you when it happens, e.g. I'll mess it up or I'm such a failure. They'll never help me. It's all going to end really badly.

Continue to think that thought for a little while, repeating it out loud for 30 seconds.

Next, carry on thinking that thought, but this time try repeating a specific phrase in front of it. The phrase is: 'I notice I'm having the thought that ...' e.g. 'I notice I'm having the thought that I'll mess it up.' Repeat this a few times: 'I notice I'm having the thought that ...'

Next, carry on thinking that thought, but this time add a slightly different phrase in front of it. This time the phrase is: 'I notice at the moment I'm having the thought that ...' e.g. 'I notice at the moment I'm having the thought that I'll mess it up.' Repeat this a few times: 'I notice at the moment I'm having the thought that ...'

What do you notice when you call out your thoughts in this way?

Another approach is to change how we experience the thought, to take away its power and make it less believable. When you reduce the thought to a meaningless collection of sounds it can have little effect. You can also use this approach to deal with your unassertive inner voices which you explored on page 200.

DISEMPOWERING THE THOUGHTS

Think of some unhelpful words that you use or think about to describe yourself or difficult, unhelpful or destructive thoughts that stop you achieving what you want to do, e.g. 'I'm too slow, passive, overqualified, untidy, disorganised.'

Now pick one and say it over and over, repeatedly, so the words run into one another and it just becomes a meaningless collection of sounds.

Now pick another and say it very very fast or very very slow, really strrreeeechhhhing out the sound. Keep repeating.

Now pick another and say it in a funny voice, like Mickey Mouse, or a sat nav or maybe a high squeaky voice or a low booming one. Say it like someone who makes you laugh. Say it like a two-year-old. Keep repeating.

You can say all these out loud or you can say them silently in your head. Whatever technique you use, you are taking steps to reduce the power that the thoughts have over you. Keep practising with new and sillier voices.

What other ways can you remove the power from disruptive or unhelpful thoughts?

During this chapter you have learnt some techniques of emotional intelligence.

※ *Emotional intelligence is the ability to pay attention to your own internal emotional world.*

※ *Emotional intelligence is using your increased knowledge to guide your thinking and actions.*

Emotional intelligence helps you:
- reduce stress and pressure
- feel more in control of your thoughts and feelings
- avoid being hijacked by your emotions
- communicate more authentically
- feel happier
- develop healthier relationships
- be more assertive with yourself

Emotional intelligence requires ongoing awareness and practice. It is a quality valued in leaders. People who develop and use their emotional intelligence skills recognise and understand emotions in themselves and others. They are less likely to turn to unhealthy ways to manage their mood (such as alcohol or non-prescription drugs). They are more likeable and less likely to experience significant mental health symptoms such as anxiety or depression.

Keep it in balance

Explore a variety of the techniques in this chapter. The over-riding cause of stress is lack of balance in your life. Everyone's perfect balance is different.

Get the balance right for you. On their death beds, or in old age, people are unlikely to say, 'I wish I'd spent more time doing housework' or 'I wish I'd spent more time at work.' It's more likely to be 'I wish I'd taken more risks' or 'I wish I'd had more time with my family' or 'I wish I'd had more fun.'

A final note on stress is that said by Nadine Stair from Louisville when she was 87 years old:

> *If I had my life to live over, I'd try to make more mistakes next time. I would relax. I would limber up. I would be sillier than I have been this trip. I would be crazier. I would be less hygienic. I would take more chances. I would take more trips. I would climb more mountains, swim more rivers, watch more sunsets ... I would eat more ice-cream and less beans. I would have more actual troubles and fewer imaginary ones. You see, I am one of those people who lives prophylactically and sanely and sensibly, hour after hour, day after day. Oh, I have had my moments and, if I had to do it all over again, I'd have more of them. In fact I'd try to have nothing else. Just moments, one after another, instead of living so many years ahead each day. I have been one of those people who never goes anywhere without a thermometer, a hot water bottle, a gargle, a raincoat, and a parachute. If I had it to do over again, I would go places and do things and travel lighter than I have.*
>
> *If I had my life to live over, I would start bare-footed earlier in the spring and stay that way later in the fall. I would play hooky more. I wouldn't make such good grades except by accident. I would ride on more merry-go-rounds. I'd pick more daisies.*

Nadine Stair

Summary and action

In this chapter you've tried lots of techniques to reduce and deal with pressure and stress. Be kind to yourself and use your emotional intelligence and common sense to keep you fit and well, emotionally, mentally and physically.

Further optional reading

Chade-Meng Tan – *Search Inside Yourself: The Unexpected Path to Achieving Success, Happiness (and World Peace)* (HarperOne)

Michael Sinclair and Matthew Beadman – *The Little ACT Workbook* (Crimson Publishing)

Robin Hills – *The Authority Guide to Emotional Resilience in Business* (Authority Guides)

Jill Dann – *Emotional Intelligence in a Week* (Teach Yourself)

Caroline Adams Miller – *Getting Grit* (Sounds True)

 Remember your 'me time'. Build in some time each day to do something for yourself. It's a great de-stressor.

Action

What action are you now going to take to ensure your stress levels stay healthy?

Here are some suggestions:
- this week I'll look into yoga classes at the gym
- I'll use the two-minute release exercise before my presentation
- I'll ask friends at lunch tomorrow about what works for them to deal with stress
- tonight I'll schedule some 'me time' into the diary for the rest of the month
- tomorrow night I'll do the thought questionnaire
- I'll request a mindfulness book for my birthday

Write yours here:

Specific Action   **By When?**

Profile *Hilary M. Jones*

Job title: Writer, trainer and yoga teacher

I've always been independent and a bit alternative. But, growing up in the south of Birmingham, I saw these as things that stopped me from fitting in rather than qualities to be nurtured. But this essence of me didn't go away and the older I got, the more I questioned the rules and what was expected of women in society. Whilst my older sister entered an unhappy marriage at 24 and quickly had two children, I went to university to study environmental science and then to do a PhD and post-doctoral research. I told my parents to spend the money they had saved for my wedding – there was never going to be one.

I moved out of academic research, feeling that the environment was cut-throat and ego-driven. Perhaps if there had been a positive, female role-model to inspire me, I would have continued. But there wasn't. Instead, long hours, poor health and estrangement from family were worn as badges of honour. To me those people were just ill and unhappy. I quit my postdoctoral research position and ran away to the south of France, where I hiked 500 miles across the Pyrenees, revelling in the freedom and the beauty of the mountains and carrying everything I owned in my backpack.

I've always been good with people and after I returned from my adventure I worked for several years in training and development in universities. I became an 'expert' in working with PhD students. But sometimes the work felt a bit hollow, as though I could be doing something with more meaning. I changed jobs and cities, but the feeling got worse rather than better. I felt like I was helping already privileged people get well-paid jobs.

During this time, I got into yoga and did a teaching qualification. When I moved to Sheffield, I began to do quite a lot of yoga teaching alongside my job in the Careers Service – and soon I earned enough from yoga to cover my mortgage. I decided to quit my career and take a 'Radical Sabbatical' trying out lots of different careers to see what I might want to do next. It was sad that most of the comments in my leaving card were that my colleagues thought I was very brave, and that they envied me.

My Radical Sabbatical has been going on for almost two years now, and I wonder whether I will ever have a 9–5 job again! I teach ten yoga classes a week and deliver various freelance training courses. I also run residential weekends of yoga, art and meditation in beautiful locations around the country. I've recently got involved with a conflict resolution charity, where I use my data analysis skills together with my creativity to make infographics for their reports and funding proposals. I've studied organic farming, plumbing and plastering, which have all been good fun (I haven't ruled out starting up my own plumbing business!) and gained specialist qualifications in Access, Word and Excel. I've also trained in narrative therapy, which is a wonderful, kind and creative way of counselling and inspired me to write a book on women's lives and career stories.

My partner and I are soon to become adoptive parents. He will take the parental leave and I will continue to work part-time and freelance, which means we'll have a wonderful year together getting to know our little one.

I'm very pleased that I didn't follow the path society had in mind for me. I've taken a long hard look at status and consumerism and decided that, for me at least, health and happiness lie in an entirely different direction.

Learning points

- Your instincts are one of the most amazing gifts you've been given. If a certain career or role doesn't feel right, then it isn't right. Keep trying until you find something that fits.
- Society will try to put you in a box. Resist if that doesn't work for you.
- Nurture your best qualities. They are with you for your lifetime and will bring you joy and fulfilment.

> *I think the best role models for women are people who are fruitfully and confidently themselves, who bring light into the world.*

Meryl Streep

What Are You About?

Objectives
- to promote a positive image of you
- to achieve the visibility you need to match your values and achieve your goals

This chapter is important because

- today's workplace is competitive
- people need to know what makes you unique
- perceptions are important
- good performance is the foundation of your brand

Contents
- showcasing your good performance
- your Personal Brand
- your message
- your public relations campaign
- your visibility
- be positive
- be memorable!
- summary and action
- profile of Bethan Crowley

Showcasing your good performance

Most of us feel better about ourselves when our good performance is recognised, but recognition only comes when people can see how well you are doing.

Even if your goal is clear to you, the impression you give of yourself may prevent others perceiving you in ways that help you reach your goals.

By consistently staying late and conscientiously doing extra work Chloe thought she was creating a good impression that would help her promotion prospects. She believed she was demonstrating that she was committed, keen and hard-working. Unfortunately her director perceived this behaviour as demonstrating that she was overstretched, unable to cope and obviously not ready for promotion.

The idea of consciously working on the impression you create about yourself may seem to suggest that you are phoney, trying to be something you are not; a superficial or manipulative person.

The opposite is true. Your aim is that people perceive you accurately. This means being more confidently yourself and putting the authentic 'you' on show. People need to have the clearest impression of you so they know who you are, what you are all about, what you have to offer and what you want. Just hoping people will notice you won't get you promotion, access to opportunities or a pay rise. It's more effective to take the initiative and make sure people know about the real you.

If you don't think about the impression you create, it may explain why:
• interviews seem to go well but you never get the job
• your friends don't take your idea of being a team leader seriously
• your suggestions are always ignored
• you get taken for granted by friends and family
• your aspirations surprise people

Your Personal Brand

We all make instant judgements of people based on limited information. Will this person be interesting to talk to? Can this person help me? Will I like this person? Apart from those who know you well, such as close personal friends and family, most people judge you primarily by your personality, reputation, behaviour and past performance. Your Personal Brand is an instant label that people apply to you based on these elements. You may be completely unaware of it.

If you want to:
- influence how you are perceived
- affect judgements that are made about you
- shape people's impression of what sort of person you are

then you have already just thought about your Personal Brand.

 Don't compromise yourself honey. You're all you've got.

Janis Joplin

You want your Personal Brand to support and reinforce what you're aiming to achieve in life, rather than undermining your efforts.

Your Personal Brand should:
- reflect your values
- connect with your purpose in life
- support the maintenance of positive relationships
- demonstrate you being the 'you' that you want to be
- tell people what to expect of you
- allow people to 'get' who you really are
- show what is unique and different about you
- be stable and durable
- influence how you are perceived
- excite you, or at least give you a warm glow
- feel comfortable

You know your values (Chapter 3). You have set goals (Chapter 6). You are becoming more authentically you through assertiveness and emotional intelligence (Chapters 7, 8 and 9). You are making relationships that support you (Chapter 5). You have audited your transferable and technical skills (Chapter 4). All the building blocks of your Personal Brand are already in place.

BRANDING QUESTIONNAIRE

The questions that follow will give insights into what your Personal Brand is all about to help with the exercises that follow.

I am known for ....
e.g. I am known for getting things done on time.

By this time next year I will be known for ....
e.g. By this time next year I will be known for establishing a new process to deal with complaints.

I am trusted with/to ....   because ....
e.g. I am trusted to help new starters because I am friendly and supportive.

I stand out from my colleagues/co-workers because ....
e.g. I stand out from my co-workers because I personally sign all the letters I send out.

I have credibility in ....   because ....
e.g. I have credibility in making supplier choices because I have commercial experience.

I make a difference with/by/to ....
e.g. I make a difference by listening and re-telling stories accurately.

I am different from ………..   because ………..
e.g. I am different from other officers because I trained via an apprenticeship.

What separates me from others like me is ………..
e.g. What separates me from others like me is my experience in trauma counselling.

You want me on your team because ………..
e.g. You want me on your team because I can see everyone's point of view and mediate good agreements.

As well as thinking about the impression you want to create you need to gather raw material about how others see you. This useful feedback highlights any gaps between perception and reality, between how you are seen and how you really are. Then you can decide if you need to change anything.

After you have written your answers on the previous page also collect responses from a trusted friend/mentor or your manager. Gathering this data is vital brand research.

Your message

How you choose to represent yourself to the world says something about you. What your Personal Brand is all about needs to be communicated to the people who need to know. This is your message.

Commercial organisations analyse the attributes and reputation of their brands, hone their 'brand message' and communicate it consistently. Popular brands therefore can be summarised in a few words, for example:

Audi: Luxury, sportiness, technological advances, four rings, performance.
Marks and Spencer: Reliable quality, customer service, 'not just food – M&S food', underwear.
Apple: Innovation, connected technology, aspirational, 'i-gadget', intuitive design.
Cadbury: 'Glass and a half', CDM, comforting, universal chocolate, philanthropy.

Imagine your Personal Brand. What are the five or six words that describe it? These are the words someone would use to describe or recommend you.

Do these words communicate the message you want to give to the world about who you are and what you stand for? If not change them.

What do you currently do that demonstrates the impression that you want to create? e.g. always gets projects done to deadlines; creates a friendly and supportive atmosphere with colleagues; shows flexibility when meetings are rescheduled.

What can you do, that you are not currently doing, that would demonstrate the impression you want to create? e.g. proactively speak to your manager about opportunities; approach another department to collaborate.

The message you put across should:
- show to those around you what you offer
- demonstrate the benefits of engaging with you
- prove it with evidence
- be positive
- be memorable
- be consistent

Your public relations campaign

The only way to be sure those around you have the right impression of you is to tell them. This is your PR campaign. Tasters, free gifts and demonstrations are ways of letting customers try out products without paying, in the hope that they will then want to buy.

In the same way you can demonstrate how great you are via job shadowing, internships, secondments or attachments to different departments as well as 'acting' roles, taking on a job temporarily to cover for the substantive post holder.

Other ways of demonstrating what you have to offer, without anyone paying any extra money for you, are:
- volunteering to do things
- getting yourself onto project groups
- representing your boss or organisation at meetings or events
- organising events, meetings, conferences, celebrations
- having bright ideas

There is a fine line between this approach and being walked all over. Remember that you're doing this to demonstrate your skills and abilities. The moment you feel you're being taken for granted is the moment to review your strategy.

 PR fails where there is no integrity.

Vivienne Sonia Segal

Keep your public relations going by making sure you tell people about the 'new improved you' when you have new skills, qualifications, additional experience or a greater commitment to what you're doing. Widen the scope of your public relations campaign to match your new goals.

Your visibility

Harvey Coleman's statistics (see page 42) show that 60% of whether you get recognition and access to opportunities depends on your visibility, so it's worth thinking about.

Visibility means people knowing your

- name and face
- personality
- achievements
- potential

Some ways of doing this are:

- making new contacts and keeping in touch with existing ones
- getting involved in social/sports/charity activities
- organising or co-ordinating activities or events
- maintaining an appropriate social media presence
- nominating yourself for awards and prizes
- ensuring you are correctly credited for things you do/achieve
- speaking up about issues important to you
- sharing your expertise with others
- sharing positive feedback that you receive (testimonials)
- being memorable – in a good way!
- writing ...
  - your own blog and contributions to other relevant blogs
  - articles in your organisation's internal press/website
  - articles in professional magazines/journals/websites
  - research or evaluation or opinion or project reports (with byline)
  - a book, or a chapter in a book or an e-book or 'how to' guide
  - authoritative posts on professional forums or social media

We all have personal brands and most of us have already left a digital footprint, whether we like it or not. Proper social media use highlights your strengths that may not shine through in an interview or application and gives the world a broader view of who you are. Use it wisely.

Amy Jo Martin

How are people going to remember you? You'll have to tell them that you exist, what you want and that you're valuable. And you'll probably have to tell them over and over again. Research about changing stereotypes shows that people have to have the stereotype in their head challenged EIGHT times before they change their mind. So it's a matter of grabbing every opportunity to remind people about you, your work, your goals and aspirations.

Source: Age UK – https://tinyurl.com/yb9s8hdb

Demonstrate the benefits

Very often, people describe themselves solely in terms of what they are or have. Talking in terms of benefits means adding how these aspects of yourself will benefit the people you currently interact with (or want to in the future).

Write down at least four features of yourself and work out the corresponding benefit:

Feature about me (quality, experience, circumstances, etc.)	Benefit to your contacts (what it does positively for them)
e.g. I have a degree	*I am able to research thoroughly and make informed decisions based on facts.*
e.g. I'm calm under pressure	*When deadlines are tight and things go wrong I stay focused and get the job done.*

Most people do not promote themselves in this way. They support their application for a job, their proposal for a revised holiday rota or whatever, by emphasising how it would help them, without considering the effect on, and potential benefits to, those they're trying to influence.

From now on, stop and put yourself in the other person's shoes.

Prove the results with evidence

When products are advertised, the manufacturers always focus on the results you will get – it uses less energy, will save you time, and so on! Promote yourself in the same way with the messages you give about you. The more specific and clear you are with the evidence about your value, the more effective your message will be.

Work out at least four examples of real evidence of how valuable you are:

Feature about me	Prove it with evidence
e.g. I'm good at client relationships	*We retained a big contract because I regularly called the client, asked their opinions about updates and explained things using their language, not jargon.*

Be positive

Adverts do not point out the things that are unhelpful about a product, or remind us of how the product doesn't work, but people do. It is not unusual to hear people say negative things like 'This job is boring', rather than 'I'm ready for more responsibility'.

Develop five really good, positive things to say about yourself and be able to back them up with evidence:

1.

2.

3.

4.

5.

Be memorable!

Things about you that make you different or special in some way also make you more memorable. These things are useful ingredients in your positive message and will make you:

- stand out
- preferable to the competition
- be more convincing
- seem more valuable
- new and fresh
- special
- different
- unique
- appear to be the best
- and above all – memorable

⌐ *Think of one thing about you that makes you memorable:*

Poppy was recently asked to give a short talk to another department. Afterwards the organiser sent her an email congratulating her on her good presentation skills.

Poppy also forwarded the email to her immediate boss and her boss's boss. It then went up the line. A few days later she had six congratulatory emails in her inbox and Poppy had successfully increased her visibility at a more senior level.

Meetings are good opportunities to make yourself and your views known. Even when they are done via conference calls, Skype/Zoom or similar online apps, the same principles apply. However, meetings can be fraught with difficulties and it is all too easy to be overlooked and become invisible.

If this tends to happen to you, remember 'The Mouse at the Meeting' law. This says that unless you say something within the first 10 minutes of the meeting, the chances are that you won't say anything at all. Watch the Mouse at the Meeting law at work – there's a lot of truth in it!

Make a point of speaking up within those all-important 10 minutes – anything to get yourself heard and noticed and to break the ice, especially if the meeting is a conference call so you cannot be seen. You'll then find it much easier to speak up later on.

Some ideas that have worked for other women are:
- checking out the agenda or the objective of an item on it
- building on someone else's point
- agreeing with or checking understanding on someone else's point

PUT YOURSELF ACROSS POSITIVELY

Give a two-minute positive talk about yourself.

If you're not used to speaking positively about yourself, try practising with a group of family, friends or colleagues, or, if that's not possible, record the talk and play it back the following day. If others join in, give each other feedback on how positively you come across and where you let yourself down.

This is an opportunity to really blow your own trumpet, so be as outrageous as you like! Get feedback on:
- what you felt was positive about the way you came across
- what you felt was negative about the way you came across
- where you felt you sold yourself short
- were you being modest?
- were you believable?
- were you over the top?
- what did you learn from or have reinforced by this exercise?

So what?

Having looked at aspects of your Personal Brand – the impression you create, how you are perceived – what do you want to do about it? Nobody goes around thinking of all these things all the time, but it is important to be clear and consistent in your message, or you run the risk of confusing people around you.

This takes time and effort. Every campaign needs investment and commitment at the beginning to get it moving. You may now be facing being more assertive, making new contacts by networking, volunteering to give a talk or setting up a blog.

Take small steps, and persevere. People may not notice your first few blog posts or may laugh when you suggest inviting the CEO to your department summer party. Taking this strategic approach may make you vulnerable to accusations of big-headedness or being ruthlessly ambitious. Stick to it whatever they say. People's memories are very short, and your personal thank-you card from the CEO and 1000 blog followers will speak for themselves in a few months' time!.

Summary and action

In this chapter you've looked at why your profile and Personal Brand building are important. You've thought about and researched how you are perceived and the impression you create. Your Personal Brand projects the real you, so that people can see the authentic you and what you can do. The next chapter gives you practical tips about presenting yourself positively.

YOUR PERSONAL RESOURCE BANK

Go to page 285 and add your benefits and evidence.
On page 286, add the things that make you special and/or different.

Action

What action are you now going to take to build your Personal Brand?
Here are some suggestions:

- next week review my LinkedIn profile
- ask Brianna tomorrow how to design a better email signature
- prepare for and ask three question at next week's project meeting
- introduce myself at the next nursery school meeting and share some of my ideas
- join the community newsletter distribution list this month so I can contribute and share my experience from running the playgroup
- go with Verena when she visits Purchasing, so I can meet the team

Write yours here:

Specific action   **By when?**

Profile *Bethan Crowley*

Job Title: Police Officer
Organisation: Avon and Somerset Police

I wouldn't say I was a 'lost' teenager but, shy and quiet, I certainly felt I didn't quite fit, floating at the edges of crowds with no solid friendship group.
My lack of confidence was compounded by bullying as I developed from a 'chubby' kid into an overweight teenager. I felt I had to be better, thinner, cooler or prettier; always opposite to the insult of the day. Anxiety around food and my size continued into my adult years.

I did OK in school despite this, although my weight and confidence continued to yo-yo throughout university. Approaching graduation with a career in education in mind, I made a mad, spur of the moment decision, going to China for a year to teach. It was an amazing, life changing experience, planting a little seed of confidence that had been missing for years. Although this ebbed away on my return to the UK, something else had lingered in the back of mind since I was a kid. I was working in a nursery when, encouraged by my partner, I took a deep breath and made a big change, moving into policing.

The first day of training gave me an overwhelming sense of excitement, infused with nerves. There were ups and downs as my life changed, professionally and personally, over those first few months. Policing can be a quite different working environment and I saw things that my friends would never see in their work. Dealing with confrontation on a daily basis, I found an authority I hadn't had before; it changed me as a person, in a good way.

I was left with a feeling of weakness when, soon after my initial training, I received a diagnosis of anxiety. The anxiety coupled with the shift work had affected connections with friends and contributed to the relationship with my partner breaking down. Although the diagnosis had been years in the making, I worried about the potential stigma. How would my organisation react? I became convinced that I'd lose the job I'd worked so hard for.

I received incredible support, though, and slowly I was able to manage my anxiety so it no longer had a significant effect on my day to day life. My confidence still wasn't where I wanted it to be, my seed of self-doubt having grown into a small tree! A year ago Springboard was recommended to me. I'd never heard of it and wasn't entirely sure what it was. Unbeknownst to me I had entered one of the most supportive rooms I think I'd ever been in. After a lifetime of trying to fit in, all of a sudden I didn't feel like the odd one out. I felt I could talk about and share my experiences and goals for the future and maybe get a handle on them too.

I'm pretty sure without it I would be years behind in my career goals, since fresh out of the 'Springboard box' I applied for and got my real dream job. Everything is now heading in the direction I want, under my control. My work continues to flourish. I'm increasing my responsibilities, not only handling them but thriving on the challenge.

Springboard has given me confidence to look after my own wellbeing. I took on a nutrition coach (another Springboard networking connection) and for the first time have a real, healthy relationship with food, exercise and my body. Now I am thriving personally, professionally and from a health perspective I am truly excited to see where this new journey takes me in my life and career. Springboard has been the catalyst for that and has exceeded the expectations I had at the first workshop.

Learning points

- It is never too late to take control of your own issues, no matter how ingrained they are or how big or daunting they seem.
- Professional help can seem terrifying, but is often extremely worthwhile. Take that step. It's OK to talk.
- Whatever form your network takes, take strength from it. Let them in and let them help and support you.
- Even if that first step feels like more of a leap, take it. You can make that move; you are not a tree.

NOTES

11

> *She who gets hired is not necessarily the one who can do the job best, but the one who knows the most about how to get hired.*

Natasha Josefowitz – *Paths to Power*

Presenting the Best You

Objective
- to put your own message across effectively

This chapter is important because

- the impression you create and your visibility contribute to your getting the role
- the application gets you the interview
- casual conversations can give lasting impressions
- your Personal Brand is being built every day
- many organisations have an open system of competition

Contents
- applying for roles
- *curriculum vitae*
- covering emails/letters
- interviews
- other formal conversations
- summary and action
- profile of Fiona McGovern

If you want to move yourself on to the next step, the messages you generate need to have a positive effect. A good application gets you the interview; a good interview gets you the role; the impression you create day-to-day builds your own public relations campaign. On-line job search websites often require a short description of yourself to catch the eye. The same principles apply.

This chapter is a practical one, full of tips and do's and don'ts. They are all straightforward common sense, but, as so often with common sense, it's good to be reminded. It covers the key elements of applications. These elements are relevant to getting a job, a place on a project team or a volunteer position.

Applying for roles

Whether you're applying for something internally or from outside an organisation, at some point you'll encounter a written application process, be asked for your CV and experience an interview. Don't be put off by unclear job descriptions or vague adverts – use all the work you've just done in Chapter 10 as your raw material and think of your application as the means for communicating it.

The Hay Group's 'Women's Work' report revealed a significant gap in motivation and ambition levels between men and women, as well as fundamental differences in what drives people in the workplace.

According to the study, men are 73% more likely than women to describe themselves as highly motivated at work. More than half of men (54%) describe themselves as ambitious, compared with just 42% of women.

Men are also 62% more likely to be doing their dream job than women, with two-thirds (59%) of men stating their job is well matched to their skills and abilities, compared with just two-fifths (41%) of women.

Source: www.haygroup.co.uk

HR professionals say that women don't apply for positions because they don't feel they fit all the criteria perfectly. They also tell of how men tend to adopt the opposite attitude – if I've got one of the requirements mentioned, it's worth a try. So is it that women aren't ambitious, lack confidence or have an unrealistic view of how ready they need to be for the next role? Have a go anyway and you may surprise yourself by getting appointed and then finding that you are good at it!

Source: www.haygroup.co.uk

Applying from outside

If you're applying from outside an organisation do your homework. E.g.

- check out the organisation's website and social media feeds to get information and some clues about the tone or style your application needs, e.g. their brand, style, products, services, what they say about working for them, annual results, etc.
- visit their head office or a local branch and pick up any literature you can, e.g. annual report, newsletter, etc.
- read the relevant trade/industry magazines or websites and familiarise yourself with current topical issues
- talk to anyone you know who knows someone who works there, or in a similar organisation
- download or get an application form or review the online process as early as possible, so you can be thinking about the format and learning more about how the organisation works
- experience the organisation in whatever way that you can, e.g. walk through the premises if they are open to the public, sign up to their website or newsletter or buy something as a customer

Written applications

Tailor each one specifically to the role you are applying for.

Some nuts and bolts

- ALWAYS get it checked for spelling and sense (not just with spellcheck)
- avoid gimmicks and unusual fonts
- be consistent in the way you present information, i.e. starting with the

present and moving into the past
- save or make a copy for your interview preparation
- make sure you have followed any specific instructions, e.g. provided correct links to an online portfolio or names of three referees
- address their criteria. Applications will be screened out immediately if you haven't shown how you fulfil their essential criteria

Getting your message across

- refer to the role description or advert
- make it results orientated, not just a list of what you are/were responsible for
- only include information that supports your case
- anticipate what they're looking for and address this head on
- be ENTHUSIASTIC
- use every space to tell them what you want to tell them
- make yourself different, e.g. instead of 'fitness' as an interest, be more specific – 'open water swimming'. Instead of 'crafts' – 'hand-made cards'
- aim to influence the content of your interview by what you put on your application form
- if you know the organisation works with competencies then give evidence to prove your ability in the required competency areas
- make it clear that you have read the job description thoroughly and if you have been to talk to someone already doing the job, or to other people in the organisation, refer to your conversations
- translate your organisational or professional jargon so that the reader can relate to what you're saying
- because of legislation there is no need to give your age – add it only if it helps your application
- use action verbs that convey energy. For example: 'managed' rather than 'was responsible for managing'

GET YOUR RESULTS ACROSS

Practise describing your last two roles in terms of results and what you achieved. Don't be modest. Use 'I achieved' not 'we achieved'.

Role title   **Results/Achievements**

Curriculum vitae

Organisations often ask you to apply by sending your *curriculum vitae*. This is your opportunity to write your own sales brochure. Your CV is, literally, the story of your life, so it's up to you what you say and how you tell the story.

A potential employer or project lead will usually use a CV as a way of screening you 'out' and will make that decision within 15 seconds. So you have 15 seconds to screen yourself 'in'!

There is also no such thing as a standard CV – you will need to rewrite it and pitch it differently for each application. In addition, you may have some basic biographical details for networking which you feel represent you generally. Check out your CV against the tips that follow.

Nuts and bolts

Follow the guidelines already given, plus:
- keep it concise, three pages or less if possible
- make sure it's well laid out and easy to read
- show your first draft to someone who will give you constructive feedback
- be prepared to rewrite it several times for each application

Content

- start with your name, address, contact phone number and email address
- education and qualifications, with the best bits first. This can go after your career history if it's not your strong point
- employment or volunteering – start with your most recent post, as it's likely to be the one of most interest to the reader, and then work backwards
- use the key words from their advert. Some organisations scan CVs without reading them first and use artificial intelligence to search for key words
- describe career breaks as you would a period of paid employment. Refer to them as, for example, 'managing a home' and describe what you achieved; 'remodelled garden using recycled resources, set and followed budget to save for training course', etc.
- consider how to present redundancy, volunteering and self-employment, and how these experiences demonstrate your abilities
- think 'portfolio' career if you have a mixture of experiences. This may be something that you consciously work on extending, or a pattern that you identify with the benefit of hindsight
- give each role title and organisation. Outline your responsibilities in one sentence for the most recent roles. Follow this with a list of three to six notable achievements to prove how valuable you were. Roles more than 15 years ago simply need the title, organisation and years
- include other information only if it helps your case, e.g. achievements outside paid employment
- conclude with items to list under 'interests'. Select them carefully, and make them interesting and different

If you have an old CV, compare it with someone else's and consider what you could have done better.

YOUR PERSONAL RESOURCE BANK

Turn to page 287 now and enter the key details you'll need to write any CV. It will help you to meet the deadline for applications, as you'll always have the key data to hand.

Covering emails/letters

CVs and application forms do not, strictly speaking, need covering emails/letters, as they more or less speak for themselves. However, we suggest you use every opportunity to promote yourself and make yourself different, so always send a short personalised email/letter:

- maximum of one side of A4
- make it clear which job you are applying for. They may be recruiting for several at the same time
- highlight and refer them to the best bits of your CV or application form
- condense your sales pitch into one short paragraph and tell them what's best or special about you
- the covering letter may become detached. So don't rely on it
- EXPRESS ENTHUSIASM – it's a rare ingredient!

Interviews

All your work in this book will be excellent preparation for interviews. Revise any chapters you consider will be important in applying for a particular role, check your personal resource bank and in particular take any action needed to strengthen your Personal Brand:

- refer back to the job description or advertisement. Use your skills audit on pages 84–86 to see how you fit
- don't be put off if you don't fit all the criteria. Job adverts are written for the perfect person, who rarely exists. When it gets to the interview, they're looking for the best person from the ones who've applied
- consider the interviewers' needs – what are they looking for? Make sure you address this in your application

- what will have been sparked off in their minds by reading your application? For example, if you've put down some very impressive achievements, they may want to know how you went about them, or what you enjoyed most about them
- how could what you say be misinterpreted? For example, if you overdo your enthusiasm to learn new things, it could be interpreted that you may not pay attention to the run-of-the-mill aspects of the job
- an interview is a two-way process – prepare in advance questions you could not have found answers to by your own research. Do not ask questions about things you should have discovered for yourself. Take a notebook into the interview with your questions written down and don't be afraid to refer to it or take notes on what you are told
- be prepared to let them know what you're good at – that's what interviews are about
- appear calm – the interviewer(s) may also be observing how you deal with the stress of an interview

About the practical arrangements

- if possible, discover where you come in the order of the day. If you are the 10th person they've interviewed that day, you'll need to pep up your performance to make yourself memorable. Equally so if you're the first – they'll still be settling down, and will 'warm up' on you
- find out how long you've got, so you can keep an eye on the time and ensure that you've covered all your main points before time runs out
- plan your journey – aim to catch the earlier train or bus to get you there well within time in case there are delays or allow traffic or puncture time if you're driving
- find out who will be on your interview panel and research them. It really helps to know their background and it goes some way to restoring the balance as they already know everything about you that's in your CV

About you

- think about the first impression you create. You need to appear comfortable in yourself and as though you fit the role you're applying for
- deal with nerves – the butterflies don't go away, but you can get them to fly in formation! Nerves help to give you an edge – and sharpen you up.

What you'll be asked

There's no set formula or list of guaranteed questions. Think about questions you may be asked specifically about your ability to do the work, the selection criteria in the role description, questions that are topical and questions that expand on the messages you've put in your application form or CV.

Don't take the questions at face value – think about what's behind the question.

Take your time before answering. Repeat the question back to check you've been understood. Have a moment of silence rather than waffling until you've realised what you want to say!

For some posts, be ready to complete a psychometric assessment before the interview – possibly on the same day. These are used increasingly and are there to reveal your strengths and good qualities for the role, and are not there to catch you out or snoop on you. Grab the opportunity, complete the test openly and honestly and welcome the valuable feedback you'll get from it. If they don't automatically give you feedback – ask for it.

Practise

Practise with a friend, colleague or another woman working through this book. It helps your nerves to say some of the positive things out loud before the big day, so that you feel more comfortable with them.

Keep applying to raise your visibility and build up your experience of interviews. Who knows, you may surprise yourself!

Compare notes with friends and colleagues to discover which topical questions are being asked currently.

Remember

- you have power in these situations – you can influence how your message is received in the way you put it across
- you are not being assessed on your value as a human being; you are being assessed for your suitability for a specific job, secondment, project, volunteer role or course

 They won't know how good you are unless YOU tell them!

MEDITATION

Before you go for an interview use any of the breathing and relaxation techniques that you have learned so far. Take a quiet and relaxing period now to imagine yourself actually being in your new role.

Imagine the location, building or site that you will be in; what the routine of your time there will be. Consider the people that you are likely to meet.

- What will they want from you?
- How will you meet their needs?
- Which of your values will you be fulfilling?
- What qualities, skills or experience will you need for the role?
- Where have you already used these qualities or skills?
- How did you gain the experience?

Allow your mind to give you as complete an impression as you can and when you finish bringing all these things to mind write down below anything you may find useful for the interview.

Afterwards

Whether you are offered the role or not, always ask for feedback on your application, interview performance and, if applicable, your psychometric assessment or any other tests you are given. Many interviewers are happy to do this over the phone and have been known to offer people alternative opportunities. It may be that you did really well, but simply weren't the appropriate person for that particular role.

Asking for feedback:
- makes you memorable
- shows them that you take your aspirations seriously
- reminds them of your enthusiasm
- nearly always makes you feel better
- helps you know yourself better

Other formal conversations

Other formal conversations are when you talk to your manager or another key person, in a situation such as an appraisal interview, a target-setting session, a performance review or a career development review. Alternatively, you may find yourself in more casual conversations after a meeting, over a cup of coffee or in a corridor, where it's just as important to create a good impression.

Use all these situations to practise all the points about putting yourself across positively, and remember:
- you are building your Personal Brand all the time
- all conversations contribute to the impression others have of you
- talk about your aspirations and achievements realistically not modestly
- ensure your message is positive and confident

When someone asks how your daily work is, use phrases such as 'I've outgrown my role' rather than 'I'm bored' and 'I'm looking for a new challenge' rather than 'It's the same old stuff'.

Here are three questions people often ask, so make some notes here for your positive replies:

'How are you getting on?'

'What are you doing these days?'

'What do you want to do next?'

Performance and career review or personal development planning meetings are a classic. How will your manager remember your particular achievements of almost a year ago, unless you remind them? It isn't being big-headed; it's being positive and self-confident.

Interviews and conversations are two-way processes, so do your preparation and go in there ready with your list of positive things to raise, e.g.
- ask for feedback on your eligibility for another role or project
- ask for training, development, mentoring or coaching
- ask for support for a secondment, work shadowing or volunteering
- list your achievements and positive feedback from others

Make a note here of things you want to raise:

After all, you've got nothing to lose – so have a go!

Summary and action

By writing applications for jobs, project roles or volunteering and preparing CVs in positive, results-orientated ways you'll increase your chances of success. By making your general conversations about yourself positive and enthusiastic you'll enhance the impression you create on a day-to-day basis.

YOUR PERSONAL RESOURCE BANK

Make a note on page 286 of your progress with interviews.

Further optional reading/contacts

Lynn Williams – *Ultimate Job Search* (Kogan Page)
Jim Bright – *Brilliant CV* (Pearson Education)

Action

What are you going to do now to make sure you project your best self?

Here are some suggestions:
- at next week's appraisal meeting ask about getting on the new development project
- tomorrow lunchtime look at the internal job website and note down how I could transfer my skills to any roles that seem interesting
- discuss with my boss on Tuesday what I want to achieve in my role
- research volunteering roles next week so I can build the experience for my CV
- sign up for LinkedIn before the end of the month and write a clear professional profile

Write yours here:

Specific action   **By when?**

Profile *Fiona McGovern*

Job Title: Community Regeneration Officer
Organisation: Ardenglen Housing Association

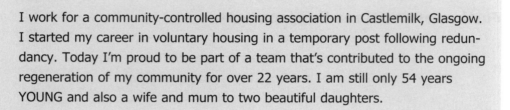

I truly believe that things happen to you for a reason.
The things that have happened throughout my life have
occurred in order to assist me to deal with life changes,
no matter how easy or hard these things are to cope with at the time.
However, this has not always been as easy to see as it is to me today.

I work for a community-controlled housing association in Castlemilk, Glasgow.
I started my career in voluntary housing in a temporary post following redundancy. Today I'm proud to be part of a team that's contributed to the ongoing
regeneration of my community for over 22 years. I am still only 54 years
YOUNG and also a wife and mum to two beautiful daughters.

It's taken quite some time, but I feel I have finally really got to know myself
and my strengths and weaknesses. This journey to changing my thinking
started 14 years ago when I attended a Springboard course, hoping to work
out how to improve my skill-set and progress my career. Springboard has also
positively affected my personal life.

We had an extremely difficult and worrying time as a family when my eldest
daughter became unwell at the age of 13. There was a long period of
uncertainty before diagnosis of an auto-immune condition. Strategies that I
had learned from Springboard helped me to support her and remain positive
through that time, holding on to hope that it would all work out.

Springboard completely changed my mindset. I overcame the prejudices that
I had about myself, and gained an understanding of my values, attitude and
beliefs. Previously, I had let others put me down; I felt inadequate due to my
education and experience. I realised that I actually had a lot going for me,
decided that it was no good being second best and used this impetus to
change old habits and develop new ways of doing things. I saw that I had
already achieved a lot in my life and that all my skills were transferable.

I started to recognise how I was influenced by the behaviour and traits of those around me and realised that my response to situations could ultimately determine the outcome. This was a huge learning point for me. I began to respond to others in a more positive manner and the results were better not just for me but for everyone.

I put together a personal development plan, setting a goal of becoming a Learning and Development Practitioner. My first objective was to undertake a professional qualification. I am very much a believer in continuous improvement. I have learnt to reflect on how I work, behave and deliver training and to change things where necessary. What keeps me going in difficult times is remembering that my work is for the benefit of the community we serve. I embrace change, building on my knowledge and understanding of our working environment and take opportunities as they come along.

One of these was a voluntary involvement in two community organisations, using my skills and knowledge to assist in agreeing constitutions, opening bank accounts and creating a fundraising strategy. Why did I volunteer my time? Simple, because I would learn from it and the knowledge put me in an even stronger position, enabling me to gain promotion to Community Regeneration Officer.

I have enjoyed the many challenges of this role. In the last 3 years I have developed a programme to engage people in communities affected by public service cuts and welfare reforms. 'The Only Way Is Up' allows me to share my knowledge and personal development practices, mentoring the programme's participants so they too can change their mindset and see the opportunities brought by change. The programme is going from strength to strength and I'm proud that it's having a positive effect in our local community.

Learning points

- I am often found to be saying, 'If I can do it – SO CAN YOU,' so what are you waiting for – SO CAN YOU!!!!
- Throughout the tough times of life you are building skills that will benefit you in the future, although it may not seem that way at the time.
- Knowing and working on yourself is an ongoing journey.

NOTES

> *Stop sitting there with your hands folded looking on doing nothing. Get into action and live this full and glorious life NOW. You have to do it.*

Eileen Caddy

Making It Happen

Objective
- to give you the support and encouragement to keep going

This chapter is important because

- you're approaching the end of this workbook
- this is the beginning of the rest of your life
- you make things happen for yourself
- it's your life – to be lived how you want it

Contents
- dealing with failure or mistakes
- building on success
- your energy and enthusiasm
- networking
- Springboard summary
- you have a choice
- action
- profile of Vandita Shukla

What have you done so far?

- you've worked your way through over 250 pages
- you've done lots of exercises – on your own and with others
- you've been asked all sorts of questions
- you've jotted down your thoughts on every subject under the sun

What does it all add up to?

- a load of rubbish?
- a lot of common sense?
- confirmation of what you already knew?
- a real eye-opener?

Whatever you think of this book, and wherever you are in your life, one thing is guaranteed: none of this will make anything happen in your life unless you really want it to.

If you stretch yourself, you run the risk of failing or making mistakes, so consider your attitude to failure, and what your strategy will be for dealing with it.

Dealing with failure or mistakes

Failure is where something has an unsuccessful or disappointing outcome. A mistake is something you didn't mean to happen. Both can feel negative and yet can be a vital part of your success. There is a world of difference between saying to yourself, 'Oh dear, I didn't mean that to happen and I am disappointed' and 'I've failed' or even worse 'I'm a failure'.

Mistakes are normal, and women who are regarded as successful have usually made loads, learned from them and then had the determination to carry on or know when to stop.

 If you're not making some notable mistakes along the way, you're certainly not taking enough business and career chances.

Sallie Krawcheck

Failure at something is almost inevitable at some point in life. It helps one see the need to keep trying new ways forward. Failure in one respect can open new doors to other possibilities. This means that a 'portfolio' career is increasingly a boon for survival. If one job or part of your work-load fails to succeed, you have others to fall back on. When one grant falls through, go for another, perhaps of a different type. When my research contract was not renewed at one point, I went on to other grants and positions, including company directorships that not only paid well, but added a new dimension to my life. I took on a host of other positions, many voluntary and without salary (except for paying for transport) and these helped improve my life skills, extend my networks and expand my knowledge-base. My work in pressing for more women in SET*, such as WiSETI and Athena, all sprung from such an event.

Learning point: Never take a failure in one part of your life to be too discouraging. Such experiences can open doors to new and better positions. A portfolio career, acquiring a number of different part-time positions, or posts that require, for example, monthly meetings only, especially for women with families, can be the solution for a successful, more flexible working life.

Nancy Lane   * science, engineering and technology

Failure and mistakes

- stretch you
- sensitise you
- show people you aren't afraid of taking risks
- can move you forward or back or sideways
- may increase your choices of what you do next
- challenge you and make you stronger
- teach you about creativity and timing
- give you practice
- can be painful
- are experienced by everyone

In people with a positive attitude, failure can bring out greater determination which, when combined with their mindset, creates a winning combination.

LEARNING FROM FAILURE AND MISTAKES

Think back to what you regard as failure or mistakes in your life and, with the benefit of hindsight, consider what they taught you. Many people say that what appeared to be a setback at the time often turns out to be a positive turning point in their life.

Occasion   **What you learnt**

How have you dealt with failure in the past?

What worked well?

What do you want to do differently in the future?

Why do I talk about the benefits of failure? Simply because failure meant a stripping away of the inessential. I stopped pretending to myself that I was anything other than what I was, and began to direct all my energy into finishing the work that mattered to me.

J K Rowling

Another part of dealing with failure positively is to be ingenious in the way you overcome the blocks that you meet. First of all:

Check you're using what's available

- find a project, secondment or volunteering opportunity to gain the experience or skills you need
- find out about funding like grants and scholarships that would get you new experience and contacts, and where others would support you
- be alert to new projects and initiatives that will get you moving again
- consider moving sideways to enable you to come back at a higher level. Use your transferable skills to do this
- extend your contacts and ask their advice
- arrange informally to shadow someone whose role you want to find out about – it need only be for a day
- find a third choice where you're in an A or B situation. Not just a compromise but a real choice to break through

Daisy qualified in sports massage in her late 30s, when on her career break. When she tried to return to work she failed to get a job in the field because, while she had the qualifications, she had no experience. She overcame this by volunteering with her local hockey team, attending matches and training session to provide on the spot therapeutic massage to the players. In her next application, Daisy was able to show that she had diagnosed and treated a wide range of injuries and ailments within a high pressure sports environment. She got the job!

Birgit was never considered for promotion because she'd become indispensable where she was. Once she realised this, she made a point of developing one of her team members to be just as capable as she was, and freed herself to be promoted.

Building on success

Success:
- boosts your confidence
- tells you you've got it right for you
- shows people what you can do.
- gives you energy
- happens every day
- encourages you
- speeds you up
- needs to be shared with others to gain recognition
- can make you complacent
- can spur you on to do more – even when it will be more difficult

Everyone has their own personal definition of success. Refer to yours on page 133.

Celebrate or mark your successes and achievements

Don't skip this part because generally you don't celebrate. In that case there's all the more reason to consider it. Celebrating is a very good way to show that you value yourself.

Celebrating:

- is fun
- gives you energy
- shows and reinforces your self-esteem
- is a reward
- establishes a progress milestone

- need not cost anything
- can be done alone or with others
- can be big or small
- may be simple or extravagant
- can be secret

You've almost finished this book. You've managed to find time in amongst everything else in your life to do the exercises. Congratulations!

What will you do to celebrate your achievements?

Your energy and enthusiasm

Along with failure and mistakes, determination is the other hallmark of the successful person, so consider for a moment how you're going to make the most of your energy and enthusiasm to keep going.

FIND ACTIVITIES TO REVIVE YOU

The things that energise you will be very personal. Here are some ideas that other women have mentioned. Are yours here?

long walks	a long bath
creative activities	yoga
an evening of movies	chat with a friend
day in bed alone	gardening
day in bed with company	a swim
sunshine	being outdoors
playing with the kids	being alone

Now add yours:

Which activities are your favourites?

Do you have a balance of activities between those:
- you do on your own and those you do with others?
- that cost nothing, very little or a lot?
- that take a long time or five minutes?

When did you last do these activities?

 Do a reviving activity daily – do one now!

Networking

Throughout this workbook we've encouraged you to renew old contacts and make new ones. If you have been working through the book in a group then we hope that you've been giving each other ideas and support all the way through. If not then we hope that you've been consciously extending your network to a wider range of people.

Online networking

It's now easy to network with people all around the world, people who you will never meet face to face, thanks to the internet. Online networking gives you quick and easy access to more people than ever before.

'Six degrees of separation' is the theory that it is possible to contact anyone in the world in only six hops. Think of 'friends of a friend' on a big scale! Research analysing Facebook use showed that the six degrees of separation drops to less than four for users of online networks.

As all of us have the possibility of linking, relatively easily, with anyone else in the world, we all have the possibility of becoming more visible, so use any network or online forum strategically, and make sure it works for you. Find out and use any online networks for your specialism, profession or field of work. We have all heard stories of potential employers routinely checking a candidate's Facebook page, as part of the recruitment process. So, as with face-to-face networking, be aware of what you're saying about yourself and with whom you are associating. Even some well-known social networks have a reputation for being anti-women or even misogynistic. Take care to protect yourself in your choice of networks.

There are so many online networks, any list immediately becomes out of date. At the time of writing, the most popular business network is **www.linkedin.com** with over 500 million users.

Networking face to face

The arrival of widespread online networking has shifted the emphasis away from face to face networking, but it's not either/or – it's both! Just as it's helpful to receive a line or two from another professional on the other side of the world, it's also important to raise your profile and get support from other people with similar aims and interests who are local to you. If you don't have access to the internet, building your contacts face to face is even more important.

To network well you'll:

- support each other and boost confidence
- share problems and information
- think in a networking way so if you can't help someone you'll think of who you know who can
- make sure you don't pull the ladder up on those coming up behind
- be objective, straightforward and tactful in your feedback to each other
- celebrate each other's successes and support each other in your failures
- still compete for the same jobs
- laugh and sometimes cry together
- strengthen each other by mutual support

The value of networking is summed up in this verse 'Support Systems':

*My right hand is being held
by someone who knows more than I,
and I am learning.
My left hand is being held
by someone who knows less than I,
and I am teaching.
Both my hands need thus to be held
for me – to be.*

Natasha Josefowitz – *Is This Where I Was Going?*

Setting up a face-to-face network

If two or three women agree to meet up for lunch to give each other ideas and support – that's a network! (Equally, many women have formed groups to network more formally and publicly.) Many networks are well established and huge, such as the Women's Institute, or more specific such as the British Association of Women in Policing. According to the Demos Report, 'Girlfriends in High Places', new 'girl' networks are challenging the power of the 'old boys' network'.

If you want to set up a more formal network, this checklist will get you started:

- what are your objectives?
- who will be eligible to attend?
- talk to your organisation and trade union if it's a network for women in that organisation
- when are you going to meet?
- where are you going to meet?
- what is the role of men: as champions, members, allies, speakers, etc.? Refer back to your objectives
- what publicity do you need?
- give it a descriptive or catchy name
- start small and let it grow
- who's going to organise it?

- respond flexibly to the needs of the group
- network with other networks – see Chapter 14
- start now!

What are you going to do to extend and maintain your networks?

joining the gym & Signed up to
Setting up volunteer with
a charity

MEDITATION

All the way through the book we have been suggesting meditations for you to enhance the work that you have been doing in each chapter. Now it is up to you to decide either to work here with your favourite one or to make up your own.

Just remember to make the quiet space, concentrate on your breathing and then allow yourself to imagine a time/place/location/situation and stay with it or select a word, phrase, colour or verse that you think will help you now.

Springboard summary

The chapters of this book give you a self-development process that you can use over and over again, either on an ongoing basis, or when you are wanting to review and make changes. Go back and do any of the exercises, or work through any of the chapters again whenever you want to.

Your Personal Resource Bank (Chapter 13) is there for you to refer to whenever you need to. Keep it up to date and it will provide you with a compact and rich source of data to help you to:

- make a decision
- reassess yourself
- write an application or CV
- go for an interview
- boost your confidence
- keep on track

In this workbook you have:
- prepared yourself
- assessed the environment you're in
- assessed yourself
- assessed the support from other people
- set your goals

Since your goals were set, you have:
- gained the information you need
- gained assertiveness skills to help you
- looked at the impression you create and your Personal Brand
- developed healthy strategies to manage stress and anxiety
- dealt with failure and success
- built your networks

How are you getting on?

If you've been working through the workbook in great detail then you have done a lot of work and covered some challenging issues.

Maybe you've worked through some bits, and skipped over others to keep up with your group, if you were working with one, or simply because they were less important to you. Or was it because they were too challenging?

If you've been reading the book without doing the exercises then we encourage you to go back and work through them, because what looks simple or obvious as you read it can be more important, meaningful, thought provoking or challenging when you actually do the work on it.

REVIEW YOUR OWN PROGRESS HERE

Did you achieve the objectives you set yourself on page 13:
- in full?

- in part?

Where did you feel challenged?

How did you meet the challenge?

What went really well and why?

Where did your support come from?

How far have you achieved the goals you set in Chapter 6?

What have you learnt that you will take into the future?

In which ways do you feel differently about yourself and your situation?

You have a choice

As you know, there is nothing magic in this workbook. All the strategies and techniques are common sense, born out of the experiences of the thousands of women attending courses and feeding back on their experiences.

Doing all the things suggested in this workbook is not enough.
You have to WANT to do it, and to continue to want to do it, so:

 You have a choice, every day, and every day can be a fresh start.

Every day you can decide whether to make the effort, take the risk and take another step on your own journey. Every day you can decide not to – you can lose your energy and let it go. If you falter, you can pick yourself up again, dust yourself off and have another go – it's up to you.

You have total freedom in your choice

No one is going to make it happen for you, you have to make it happen for yourself, and every day you can renew your commitment freely – or not.

What you do and how you do it is entirely up to you. Smply put – DO IT! It's important that you do, because that way you will become more fully yourself and be the best you can be.

Live the life that you choose for yourself – not the life that your parents (or whoever brought you up) mapped out for you, or that your partner assumes for you or that you seem to have fallen into. Make the choice, and then put it into action, through small practical steps or big dramatic leaps – whatever fits you best.

Whatever it is that you decide to do – we wish you your own definition of success in doing it!

Nelson Mandela made the following words famous as the first black president of South Africa. His quotation came from the book *Return to Love* by Marianne Williamson.

> *Our deepest fear is not that we are inadequate.*
> *Our deepest fear is that we are powerful beyond measure.*
> *It is our light, not our darkness, that most frightens us.*
> *We ask ourselves, 'Who am I to be brilliant, gorgeous, talented, fabulous?'*
> *Actually, who are you not to be? You are a child of God.*
> *Your playing small doesn't serve the world.*
> *There is nothing enlightened about shrinking so that other people won't feel insecure around you.*
> *We are all meant to shine, as children do.*
> *We are born to make manifest the glory of God that is within us.*
> *It is not in some of us; it is in everyone.*
> *And as we make our own light shine, we unconsciously give others permission to do the same.*
> *As we are liberated from our fear, our presence automatically liberates others.*

Action

What are you going to do now, to continue taking positive steps in your life?

 A journey of 1000 miles starts with a single step.
Keep taking the steps!

Profile *Vandita Shukla*

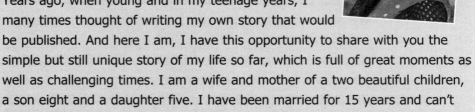

Job Title: *Executive Support Manager to National*
   People Directors
Organisation: *Royal Mail Group*

Years ago, when young and in my teenage years, I
many times thought of writing my own story that would
be published. And here I am, I have this opportunity to share with you the
simple but still unique story of my life so far, which is full of great moments as
well as challenging times. I am a wife and mother of a two beautiful children,
a son eight and a daughter five. I have been married for 15 years and can't
stop smiling.

I was born and brought up in the west of India and spent more than half of
my life there with my highly motivated Mum, ever dedicated Dad, a fun Sister
and a lovely caring Brother. I was the eldest. My Mother, as a housewife,
helped us stay focused on our education and my Dad, a bank manager,
managed the family financial needs. I still remember cycling to school with my
brother in his carrier seat and sister riding alongside and after school, riding
back home as fast as we could. Every Sunday morning with beautiful songs on
the radio our parents used to come to our rooms to wake us up with some
giggles and tickles and that is how I spent my early years of life.

Years go past and, by the time I realised, I was in university in a different
state, away from my family, studying engineering and living in a hostel. I had
moments when I was homesick and wrote letters saying how badly I missed
them although also I thoroughly enjoyed studying. My family still have those
letters and read them from time to time, which bring tears and smiles still today.

I got married in my last year of university. Life changed for me as I came to
the UK to join my husband and his family. Everything was new to me, the
language, the country, new relations and also the people. English was never
spoken in my life and the different accent also took some time for me to
understand and be able to communicate with people.

After months' wait and a few applications I finally got a job at Royal Mail as a Christmas casual postie then became a part-time postwoman. Being young and grabbing the opportunities to earn more, I worked extremely hard with two jobs and only four hours' sleep. I worked for several other high street names whilst continuing my job with Royal Mail.

We spent a few years as a couple and built some amazing memories for life and then decided to have children. While being a wife, a daughter-in-law, a mother and also a wider family member, one thing I learnt was life is not easy and it gets even tougher unless I myself make it easier. Life is full of challenges and you face them at each and every stage. Remember to keep the belief and trust in yourself and stay positive towards everything that comes your way. The confidence and faith in yourself will win you the battle no matter which kind.

Here I am now, still with Royal Mail, for 13 years, with a career journey from being a Christmas casual to an Executive Support Manager to National People Directors. When I look back in life and see how it has been, the struggles I had and how I embarked on them is always a mystery to myself. What I know for sure and so share with you all is: realise the potential within yourself. As women we have a hidden and god-gifted power that sometimes can take time to realise and come alive.

Learning points

- You don't know how strong you can be until you come across challenging situations in life or in a position at work. You will triumph!
- Remember that you are the person who can make your life easier, so choose that instead of making it more difficult, and shout when you need help, as none of us are superwomen.
- Having strong relationships with your loved ones will help you through difficulties in life; moral and emotional support empowers the inner strength.
- You can face all challenges with patience, faith and belief within yourself, and surely you will get through them.

NOTES

Your Personal Resource Bank

Objective
- to compile a reference file of useful information about yourself for future use

Your Personal Resource Bank

This chapter gives you headings under which you build up your bank of useful data about yourself. This means that you keep all the overall facts and ideas about yourself in one place, and gives you material to refer to whenever you want to review or change anything in your life. It will be particularly useful to you when you:
- apply for a project, job or volunteering role
- prepare for an interview
- face a difficult life situation
- are faced with change
- want to reset goals
- write your CV
- write an online professional profile
- make decisions
- want to revive your determination

Each chapter has valuable information for your personal resource bank. Here are handy references to key pages. Also record anything else you find useful. Write it here or start your own computer file for reference.

Change

My usual responses to change at home and at work – pages 10–11

My Qualifications

School qualifications
e.g. GCSEs, A and AS Levels, Scottish Highers and Advanced Highers, International Baccalaureate:

Other qualifications taken at school
e.g. Duke of Edinburgh Award, Queen's Guide, life-saving certificates, music certificates:

College, art school or university qualifications

e.g. BTEC, NVQs, technical qualifications, degrees, post-graduate degrees, City and Guilds, college diplomas, apprenticeships and vocational qualifications:

Courses attended where no formal qualifications were given at the end

Professional qualifications

Also include courses that you're part way through:

Qualifications I need/want to get in the future

Anything else?

VALUES

The things I value most highly – page 63

ACHIEVEMENTS

The things I have achieved – page 76
The things I want to achieve – page 77

⌐*The achievement I'm particularly proud of is:*

STRENGTHS AND WEAKNESSES

The qualities that are my strengths – page 80
The strengths as partners that I draw on to overcome weaknesses – page 80

SKILLS

Pages 84–86

TRANSFERABLE SKILLS

My best skills are: *An example of using them well is:*

In addition, other people say I am also good at:

PEOPLE

People who are actively helping me now – pages 106–109

People who I am going to ask to help me are:

Information I've found out about my contacts – pages 113–114

GOALS

ASSERTIVENESS

Situations at work where I know I can be assertive are:

Situations at home where I know I can be assertive are:

Situations where I know I can be assertive with myself are:

PRESENTING THE BEST YOU

Benefits and evidence from 'What Are You About?' – pages 235–237

Feature about me	Evidence of this	Benefit to others

Things that make me special or different are:

When I go for interviews, I know I'm good at:

The aspect I need to work on is:

MY WORK/VOLUNTEERING/EXPERIENCE HISTORY

Dates	Organisation/ department	Role	Achievements/results

MY WORK/VOLUNTEERING/EXPERIENCE HISTORY

Dates	Organisation/ department	Role	Achievements/results

MY WORK/VOLUNTEERING/EXPERIENCE HISTORY

Dates	Organisation/ department	Role	Achievements/results

MY WORK/VOLUNTEERING/EXPERIENCE HISTORY

Dates	Organisation/ department	Role	Achievements/results

OTHER THINGS I WANT TO KEEP A NOTE OF

OTHER THINGS I WANT TO KEEP A NOTE OF

Where Can I Find ...?

Organisations

Campaigning Groups

Equal Opportunities and Human Rights

Health and Wellbeing

Support for Lesbian, Bisexual, Trans and Non-binary Women

Study and Careers

Women's Networks

Relationships and Working Families

Books

Assertiveness

Disability Issues

Finance

Health and Wellbeing

Personal Development

Relationships

Sexual Orientation and Gender Identity

Skills and Careers

Women's Issues, Equality and Feminism

Organisations

Campaigning Groups

Disability Rights UK
Tel: 033 0995 0400
Email: enquiries@disabilityrightsuk.org **www.disabilityrightsuk.org**
Campaigns for equal participation in society for all. Works to protect and strengthen disabled people's rights.

Fawcett Society
Tel: 020 3598 6154
Email: info@fawcett.org.uk **www.fawcettsociety.org.uk**
Campaigning for changes in legislation to give women true equality. Also gives information. Founded during the suffrage movement in 1866.

National Alliance of Women's Organisations (NAWO)
Tel: 020 3802 0416
Email: admin@nawo.org.uk **www.nawo.org.uk**
Umbrella organisation for over 100 organisations and individuals based in England, concerned to ensure women gain access to their human rights, and to make equality between women and men a reality.

National Council of Women of Great Britain
Tel: 020 7354 2395
Email: info@ncwgb.org **www.ncwgb.org**
Umbrella organisation – regional councils, information and lobbying.

Rights of Women
Advice line: 020 7251 6577
Email: info@row.org.uk **www.rightsofwomen.org.uk**
Free legal advice and assistance for women.

The Suzy Lamplugh Trust
Email: info@suzylamplugh.org **www.suzylamplugh.org**
The leading authority on personal safety: aiming to create a safer society

and help everyone to live safer lives. Runs the National Stalking Helpline.

Womankind Worldwide
Tel: 020 3567 5930
Email: info@womankind.org.uk   **www.womankind.org.uk**
Enabling women in developing countries to take greater control over their own lives by funding practical projects.

Working Families
Email: office@workingfamilies.org.uk   **www.workingfamilies.org.uk**
UK's work/life balance charity campaigning for family-friendly workplaces and advocating for working families and working carers, especially those who are disadvantaged.

Equal Opportunities and Human Rights

Equality and Human Rights Commission
Tel: 020 7832 7800   **www.equalityhumanrights.com/en**
Independent statutory body with responsibility to encourage equality and diversity, eliminate unlawful discrimination and protect and promote the human rights of everyone in Britain. Enforces legislation on the protected characteristics: age, disability, gender reassignment, marriage and civil partnership, pregnancy and maternity, race, religion and belief, sex and sexual orientation.

Gender Pay Gap Service
          https://gender-pay-gap.service.gov.uk
Government website to search and compare gender pay gap data from organisations. All employers of 250 or more employees must report this data.

TUC Equal Rights Department
Tel: 020 7636 4030
Email: info@tuc.org.uk   **www.tuc.org.uk/research-analysis/equality**
Provides useful publications on equal rights and deals with a wide range of equality issues.

UK Feminista
Tel: 0207 061 6220
Email: info@ukfeminista.org.uk   **www.ukfeminista.org.uk**
Dedicated to supporting people to take action to create lasting change and bring about true equality between women and men.

Health and Wellbeing

Al-Anon Family Groups
Tel: 020 7403 0888 (24-hour helpline)
Email: enquiries@al-anonuk.org.uk   **www.al-anonuk.org.uk**
Provides support to anyone whose life is, or has been, affected by someone else's drinking, regardless of whether that person is still drinking or not.

Alcoholics Anonymous
Tel: 0800 9177 650
Email: help@aamail.org   **www.alcoholics-anonymous.org.uk**
Voluntary, international fellowship concerned solely with the personal recovery and continued sobriety of individual alcoholics.

All Women Count
Email: samantha@refugeewomen.co.uk   **www.allwomencount.net**
International organisation and lobbying group supporting the right to safety, dignity and liberty of migrant and refugee women.

Alzheimers UK
Dementia Helpline: 0300 222 1122
Email: via website   **www.alzheimers.org.uk**
Resources, advice and support for those affected by dementia.

Beat
Helpline: 0808 801 0677
Email: info@beateatingdisorders.org.uk   **www.beateatingdisorders.org.uk**
Champion, guide and friend to anyone affected by eating disorders.

Breast Cancer Care

Tel: 020 0345 092 0800 **www.breastcancercare.org.uk**

Email: movingforward@breastcancercare.org.uk

Information and support for anyone affected by breast cancer.

Cruse Bereavement Care

Tel: 0808 808 1677

Email: info@cruse.org.uk **www.cruse.org.uk**

Publications and national network and counselling for anyone bereaved.

Daughters of Eve

Tel: 07983 030 488

Email: via website **www.dofeve.org**

Works to protect girls and young women at risk from female genital mutilation. Raises awareness and signposts services.

Disabled Living

Helpline: 0161 607 8200

Email: info@disabledliving.co.uk **www.disabledliving.co.uk**

Offers impartial advice to disabled adults, children and older people and carers and professionals who support them on products, assistive technology and services.

Macmillan Cancer Support

Support line: 0808 808 0000

Email: via website **www.macmillan.org.uk**

Provides support, tools and inspiration to people affected by a diagnosis of cancer. Has local groups, workshops and e-learning packages.

Marie Stopes Clinic

Tel: 0345 300 8090

Email: via website **www.mariestopes.org.uk**

Independent provider of sexual and reproductive health services. Provides helplines, clinics and advice.

Mind
Tel: 0208 519 2122
Email: via website   **www.mind.org.uk**
Advice and support to empower anyone experiencing a mental health problem. Campaigns to improve services, raise awareness and promote understanding.

Mumsnet

www.mumsnet.com

Makes parents' lives easier by pooling knowledge, advice and support on everything from conception to childbirth, from babies to teenagers.

National Association for Premenstrual Syndrome
Helpline: 0844 815 7311
Email: contact@pms.org.uk   **www.pms.org.uk**
Supports individual PMS sufferers and promotes greater awareness of PMS and its treatment.

National Osteoporosis Society
Helpline: 0808 800 0035
Email: info@nos.org.uk   **www.nos.org.uk**
Charity working to improve bone health by providing support and information, driving research and influencing healthcare providers.

QUIT
Quitline: 0800 00 22 00
Email: m.hussain@quit.org.uk   **www.quit.org.uk**
Information and advice on how to stop smoking.

Samaritans
Freecall from any phone: 116123
Email: jo@samaritans.org   **www.samaritans.org**
Offering a safe space to talk any time about what's getting to you, however large or small. You don't have to be suicidal to call.

Shelter

Helpline: 0808 800 4444

Email: via the websites

England: **www.england.shelter.org.uk**

Scotland: **www.scotland.shelter.org.uk**

Wales: **www.sheltercymru.org.uk**

Charity providing advice and support on housing and homelessness.

Talk to Frank

Tel: 0300 123 6600

Email: via website   **www.talktofrank.com**

Friendly, confidential drugs advice. A–Z of drugs, live chat, advice and facts about drugs.

Women's Health Concern

Tel: 0162 889 0119   **www.womens-health-concern.org**

Email: info@womens-health-concern.org

Educates and supports women in health issues, especially gynaecological and sexual health including menopause.

Support for Lesbian, Bisexual, Trans and Non-binary Women

All About Trans

Email: info@onroadmedia.org.uk   **www.allabouttrans.org.uk**

Looks at creative ways to encourage greater understanding between trans people and the media to support better, more sensitive representation in the UK media.

LBGT Foundation

Tel: 0345 330 3030

Email: info@lgbt.foundation   **https://lgbt.foundation**

Charity delivering advice, support and an information service to the lesbian, gay, bi and trans community.

Stonewall

Tel: 020 7593 1850

Email: info@stonewall.org.uk   **www.stonewall.org.uk**

Campaigns for civil rights. To let all lesbian, gay, bi and trans people in the UK and abroad know they are not alone. Works by partnering so everyone feels free to be who they are, wherever they are.

Tranzwiki   **www.tranzwiki.net**

Online directory of groups campaigning for, supporting or assisting trans and gender non-conforming individuals.

Study and Careers

Ability Net

Tel: 0800 269545

Email: enquiries@abilitynet.org.uk   **www.abilitynet.org.uk**

Organisation to help disabled adults, children and their advisers. Focuses on use of digital technology at home, at work and in education to help people make the most of their abilities.

Career Connect

Tel: 0800 0126 606

Email: adviser@careerconnect.org.uk   **www.careerconnect.org.uk**

High quality independent careers advice for adults and young people. Has a CV builder, assessment quizzes and live chat with advisers.

National Career Service

Tel: 0800 100 900   **nationalcareersservice.direct.gov.uk**

Site with information, advice and guidance to help make decisions on learning, training and work. Skills health check, find a course, job profiles and advice phone line.

The Open University

Tel: 0845 300 60 90

Email: general-enquiries@open.ac.uk   **www.open.ac.uk**

Provider of diploma and degree programmes and short courses.

Women Like us

Email: info@womenlikeus.org.uk   **www.womenlikeus.org.uk**

Career advice and specialist recruiter for part-time and flexible roles for women to fit around family and caring commitments.

Women's Networks

Business and Professional Women UK Ltd

Tel: 01277 623867

Email: hq@bpwuk.co.uk   **www.bpwuk.co.uk**

Affiliated with BPW International, which has representation in over 100 countries. Networking, training and development, conferences, social events, and campaigning on issues affecting women.

CMI Women

Tel: 01536 207307   **www.managers.org.uk/cmi-women**

Email: membership@managers.org.uk

Subgroup of the Chartered Management Institute. Seeking to inspire and support women throughout their careers and provide a blueprint for balance so organisations can become more gender diverse.

National Federation of Women's Institutes

Tel: 020 7371 9300

Email: hq@nfwi.org.uk   **www.thewi.org.uk**

National Women's Register

Email: office@nwr.org   **www.nwr.org**

International organisation of women's groups offering opportunities for stimulating discussion of non-domestic nature.

Prowess

Email: admin@prowess.org.uk   **www.prowess.org.uk**

A network of organisations and individuals who support the growth of women's business ownership and entrepreneurship.

WISE (Women in Science and Engineering)   **www.wisecampaign.org.uk**
Campaigns for gender balance in science, technology and engineering.

Women in Banking and Finance
Email: operations@wibf.org.uk   **www.wibf.org.uk**
An independent networking group sponsored by banks and other financial organisations run by and for its members.

Women in the Law
Email: womeninthelaw@gmail.com   **www.womeninthelaw.co.uk**
To encourage, inspire and support the next generation of lawyers and women in business. Helps young women to talk to senior men and women about the profession.

Women in Property
Tel: 01462 635416   **www.womeninproperty.org.uk**
Email: membership@womeninproperty.org.uk
Creates opportunity, expands knowledge and inspires change for women working in the property and construction industry.

Women in Publishing
Email: via website   **www.womeninpublishing.org.uk**
Network to provide a forum for exchange and support and offer practical training for career and personal development.

Women on the Tools
Tel: 0330 311 0447
Email: info@womenonthetools.org.uk   **www.womenonthetools.org.uk**
Works with employers and colleges to help recruit and retain tradeswomen to tackle the skills shortage and achieve better gender balance.

Women Returner's Professional Network
Email: info@womenreturners.com   **www.women-returners.com**
Aims to facilitate the re-entry of women to education, training and employment following a career break. It provides advice, information, training opportunities, a network and an annual conference.

Women's Engineering Society
Tel: 01438 765506
Email: info@wes.org.uk **www.wes.org.uk**
Professional body representing the interests of women engineers.

Relationships and Working Families

Age UK
Helpline: 0800 055 6112 **www.ageuk.org.uk**
Network of local Age UK groups which offers a wide range of support and campaigning activities.

Carers UK
Tel: 020 7378 4999
Email: info@carersuk.org **www.carersuk.org**
Charity to support those caring for others. Provides expert advice, information and support. Connects carers through an online forum, carers' groups and volunteers.

Crysis
Tel: 08451 228 669
Email: info@cry-sis.org.uk **www.cry-sis.org.uk**
Support group for parents of excessively crying and/or sleepless babies and young children. Also support for parents of children with behavioural problems, e.g. tantrums, clinginess.

Family and Childcare Trust
Tel: 020 7239 7535 **www.familyandchildcaretrust.org.uk**
Email: info@familyandchildcaretrust.org.uk
Aims to make the UK a better place for families, focusing on childcare and the early years to make a difference to families' lives now and in the long term. Has a childcare search tool.

Family Lives
Helpline: 0808 800 2222
Email: via the website   **www.familylives.org.uk**
*Help for anyone caring for a child. Emotional support, information, the
chance to talk through problems in confidence.*

Family Mediators Association
Tel: 01355 244595   Mediation helpline: 0808 200 0033
Email: info@thefma.co.uk   **www.thefma.co.uk**
*Helps with family property and financial arrangements when parents/
families split up. Also offers training in the field.*

Gingerbread
Tel: 020 7428 5400   Helpline: 0808 802 0925
Email: via website   **www.gingerbread.org.uk**
*Promotes and supports local self-help groups for one-parent families. Also
provides expert advice and information for lone parents.*

Home-Start
Tel: 0116 233 9955
Email: info@home-start.org.uk   **www.home-start.org.uk**
*Family support group run by volunteers throughout the UK, supporting
families with at least one child under the age of five.*

Hyperactive Children's Support Group
Tel: 01243 539966
Email: hacsg@hacsg.org.uk   **www.hacsg.org.uk**
*Supports and advises parents/professionals of hyperactive and ADHD
children using dietary/nutritional therapies.*

National Autistic Society
Helpline: 0808 800 4104
Email: nas@nas.org.uk   **www.autism.org.uk**
Support for families and carers of children with autism.

National Childbirth Trust

Tel: 0300 330 0700

Email: enquiries@nct.org.uk   **www.nct.org.uk**

The NCT offers information and support in pregnancy, childbirth and early parenthood. Aims to give every parent the chance to make informed choices. There are over 400 branches throughout the UK.

Relate

Email: relate.enquiries@relate.org.uk   **www.relate.org.uk**

Provides relationship support for all kinds of people via local counsellors, self-help online tools and resources; support via telephone, live chat and webcam.

Stillbirth and Neonatal Death Society

Tel: 020 7436 7940   Helpline: 0808 164 332

Email: support@uk-sands.org   **www.uk-sands.org**

SANDS provides support for bereaved parents and their families when their baby dies at or soon after birth.

Women's Aid

Tel: 0117 944 4411 Helpline: 0808 2000 247

Email: helpline@womensaid.org.uk   **www.womensaid.org.uk**

Helps women and children who are experiencing violence in the home.

Books

This is not a definitive list but will get you off to a good start:

Assertiveness

Ken and Kate **Back** – *Assertiveness at Work* (McGraw Hill)

Dannie Lu **Carr** – *Brilliant Assertiveness* (Prentice Hall)

Deborah **Dalley** – *Developing Your Assertiveness Skills* (Universe of Learning)

Anne **Dickson** – *A Woman in Your Own Right* (Quartet)

Gael **Lindenfield** – *Assert Yourself* (Collins)

Disability Issues

Julie **Andrews** – *Dementia: The One-Stop Shop* (Profile Books)
Ian **Greaves** – *Disability Rights Handbook* (Disability Rights UK)
Mary **Jordan** – *The Essential Carer's Guide* (Hammersmith Health Books)
Motability – *Rough Guide to Accessible Britain* (download from
    www.motability.co.uk)
Ann **Thomson** – *RSI Survival Guide* (RSI and Overuse Injury Association)

Finance

Linda **Babcock** and Sara Laschever – *Ask For It: How Women Can Use
    the Power of Negotiation to Get What They Really Want* (Bantam)
Simonne **Gressen** and Karen **Pine** – *Sheconomics* (Hodder Headine)
Natalie **Spencer** – *Good Money: Understand Your Choices, Boost Your
    Financial Wellbeing* (White Lion Publishing)
Merryn **Somerset Webb** – *Love Is Not Enough: A Smart Women's Guide
    to Money* (Harper Perennial)

Health and Wellbeing

Megan **Arroll** and Christine **Dancey** – *Irritable Bowel Syndrome:
    Navigating Your Way to Recovery* (Hammersmith Books)
Julia **Buckroyd** – *Understanding Your Eating: How to Eat and Not Worry
    about It* (Open University Press)
Katharina **Dallon** and Wendy **Holton** – *The PMS Bible* (Vermilion)
Liz **Earle** – *The Good Menopause Guide* (Orion Spring)
Steve **Haines** – *Pain Is Really Strange* (Singing Dragon)
Jonathan **Horovitz** and Deane **McIntosh** – *Stress: The Psychology of
    Managing Pressure* (Dorling Kindersley)
Oliver **James** – *Contented Dementia* (Vermilion)
Chris **Jenner** – *Arthritis: A Practical Guide to Getting on with Your Life*
    (Robinson)
Elizabeth **Le Roux** – *Migraines: More than a Headache* (Dundurn Group)
Mark **Levy**, Monica **Fletcher** and Soren **Pederson** – *Asthma: Answers at
    Your Fingertips* (Class Health)

Kate **Lorig** – *Self Management of Long Term Conditions* (Bull Publishing)

Guy **Meadows** – *The Sleep Book: How to Sleep Well Every Night* (Orion)

Helen **Odessky** – *Stop Anxiety Stopping You: The Breakthrough Program for Conquering Panic and Social Anxiety* (Mango)

Ann **Patterson** – *Beating Eating Disorders Step by Step* (Jessica Kingsley)

David **Rowland** – *How I Rescued my Brain* (Scribe)

Alan **Rubin** – *Diabetes for Dummies* (Wiley)

Julia **Samuel** – *Grief Works: Stories of Life, Death and Surviving* (Penguin)

Tom **Smith** – *Living with Angina* (Sheldon Press)

Mithu **Storoni** – *Stress-Proof: The Scientific Solution to Protect Your Brain and Be More Resilient Every Day* (TarcherPerigee)

Chris **Williams** – *Living Life to the Full* (online course at https://lltf.com)

Personal Development

Caroline **Adams Miller** – *Getting Grit* (Sounds True)

Stephen R. **Covey** – *The Seven Habits of Highly Effective People* (Simon and Schuster)

Jill **Dann** – *Emotional Intelligence in a Week* (Teach Yourself)

Jinny S **Ditzler** – *Your Best Year Yet!* (Harper Element)

Rick **Hanson** – *Resilient* (Routledge)

Thomas A **Harris** – *I'm OK, You're OK* (Arrow)

Susan **Jeffers** – *Feel the Fear and Do It Anyway* (Vermilion)

Tina **Konstant** and Morris **Taylor** – *Overcoming Information Overload* (CMI)

Susan D. **Miller** – *Be Heard the First Time: A Woman's Guide to Powerful Speaking* (Capital Books)

Mind Gym – *Give Me Time* (Sphere)

Michael **Sinclair** and Matthew **Beardman** – *The Little ACT Workbook: A Mindfulness Based Guide to Leading a Full and Meaningful Life* (Crimson)

Elaine **St James** – *Simplicity: Easy Ways to Simplify and Enrich Your Life* (Thorsens)

Chade-Meng **Tan** – *Search Inside Yourself* (HarperOne)

Relationships

Jack **Adams** – *The Rules: Supporting Men to Thrive in the Here and Now* (CreateSpace)

Steve **Biddulph** – *Manhood* (Vermilion)

Steve **Biddulph** – *Raising Girls* (Harper Thorsons)

Robert **Bly** – *Iron John* (Rider)

Joanna **Coles** – *Love Rules: How to Find a Real Relationship in a Digital Age* (Harper)

Shaunti **Feldhahn** – *For Women Only: What You Need to Know about the Inner Lives of Men* (Multnomah Press)

Roskje **Hasseldine** – *The Mother-Daughter Puzzle* (Women's Bookshelf)

Anne **Katz** – *Women Cancer Sex* (Oncology Nursing Society)

Sarah **Litvinoff** – *The Relate Guide to Better Relationships* (Vermilion)

Emily **Nagoski** – *The Scientific Guide to Successful Relationships* (GIB Guides)

Lucinda **Neall** – *Bringing out the Best in Boys* (Hawthorn Press)

Robin **Norwood** – *Women Who Love Too Much* (Arrow Books)

Linda **Papadopoulos** – *The Man Manual* (Hodder and Stoughton)

Deborah **Tannen** – *You Just Don't Understand* (Virago)

Deborah **Tannen** – *That's Not What I Meant!* (Virago)

Sexual Orientation and Gender Identity

John **Browne** – *The Glass Closet: Why Coming out Is Good for Business* (W.H. Allen)

Amity Pierce **Buxton** – *The Other Side of the Closet* (John Wiley)

Anne **Dickson** – *The Mirror Within* (Quartet)

Dara **Hoffman-Fox** – *You and Your Gender Identity: A Guide to Discovery* (Skyhorse Publishing)

C.N. **Lester** – *Trans Like Me* (Virago)

Val **McDermid** and Evan **Davis** – *It's OK to Be Gay: Celebrity Coming out Stories* (Accent Press)

Emily **Nagoski** – *Come as You Are* (Scribe)

Jane **Traies** – *Now You See Me: Lesbian Life Stories* (Tollington Press)

Jenny **van Hoff** – *Modern Couple? Continuity and Change in Heterosexual Relationships* (Routledge)

Skills and Careers

Jim **Bright** and Joanne **Earl** – *Brilliant CV: What Employers Want and How to Write It* (Prentice Hall)

Richard **Bolles** – *What Color Is Your Parachute?* (Ten Speed Press)

Tony **Buzan** – *Head Strong: How to Get Physically and Mentally Fit* (Thorsons)

Steven **D'Souza** – *Brilliant Networking* (Pearson Business)

Bob **Etherington** – *Presentation Skills for Quivering Wrecks* (Cyan Books)

Nina **Grunefeld** – *The Big Book of Me: Be Your Own Life Coach* (Short Books)

Lynne **Franks** – *The Seed Handbook: The Feminine Way to Create Business* (Hay House)

Thich Nhat **Hanh** – *Calming the Fearful Mind* (Parallax Press)

Harvard Business Review – *Guide to Managing Up and Across* (HBR)

Pat **Helm**, Tammy **Hughes** and Susan K. **Golant** – *Hardball for Women: Winning at the Game of Business* (Plume Books)

Mishal **Husain** – *The Skills: From First Job to Dream Job – What Every Woman Needs to Know* (Fourth Estate)

John **Lees** – *How to Get a Job You'll Love* (McGraw Hill)

Barbara **Killinge**r – *Workaholics: The Respectable Addicts* (Key Porter Books)

John **Lockett** – *Powerful Networking* (Orion Business)

Lucy **Martin** and Bella **Mehta** – *Make It Your Business* (Springhill)

David **McNally** and Karl **Speak** – *Be Your Own Brand* (Beret Koehler)

Peter **Montoya** – *The Brand Called You* (McGraw Hill Education)

Barbara **Moses** – *What Next?* (Dorling Kindersley)

Michael **Sinclair** and Josie **Seydell** – *Working with Mindfulness* (Pearson)

Mary **Spillane** – *Branding Yourself* (Sidgwick and Jackson)

Matt **Weinstein** – *Managing to Have Fun* (Touchstone)

Susan **Wilson Solovic** – *The Girls' Guide to Power and Success* (AMA)

Jurgen **Wolf** – *Focus: Use the Power of Targeted Thinking to Get More Done* (Pearson Business)

Women's Issues, Equality and Feminism

Far too many to identify, so here are a few to get you started:

Maya **Angelou** – *I Know Why the Caged Bird Sings* (Virago)

Kat **Banyard** – *The Equality Illusion* (Faber and Faber)

Lauren **Bravo** – *What Would the Spice Girls Do? How the Girl Power Generation Grew up* (Bantam)

Kira **Cochrane** – *Women of the Revolution: Forty Years of Feminism* (Guardian Books)

Scarlett **Curtis** – *Feminists Don't Wear Pink (and Other Lies): Amazing Women on What the F-word Means to Them* (Penguin)

Susan **Faludi** – *Backlash* (Vintage)

Lois P **Frankel** – *Nice Girls Don't Get the Corner Office: 101 Unconscious Mistakes Women Make* (Little, Brown)

Clementine **Ford** – *Fight Like a Girl* (Oneworld Publications)

Farida **Khalaf** and Andrea C. **Hoffmann** – *The Girl Who Escaped ISIS* (Atria Books)

Caitlin **Moran** – *How to Be a Woman* (Ebury Press)

Zana **Muhsen** with Andrew **Crofts** – *SOLD* (Time Warner)

Vrinda **Naba**r – *Caste as Woman* (Penguin Books)

Susan **Nolen-Hoeksema** – *Women Who Think Too Much: How to Break Free of Over-Thinking and Reclaim Your Life* (Piatkus)

Susie **Orbach** – *Fat Is a Feminist Issue* (Arrow)

Sheryl **Sandberg** – *Lean In* (W.H. Allen)

Dale **Spender** – *Man Made Language* (Rivers Oram Press)

Jennifer **Uglow** – *The Palgrave Macmillan Dictionary of Women's Biography* (Palgrave Macmillan)

Jessica **Valenti** – *Full Frontal Feminism: A Young Woman's Guide to Why Feminism Matters* (Seal Press)

Natasha **Walter** – *Living Dolls* (Virago)

Natasha **Walter** – *The New Feminism* (Virago)

Margaret **Walters** – *Feminism: A Very Short Introduction* (Oxford University Press)

Index

Getting in touch

You can work through this book on your own. However, it is also designed to be used as part of the Springboard Women's Development Programme, which will give you the support and stimulation of other people and short, down-to-earth workshops to enable you to get the most out of this book.

In addition, there are other ways in which we can support you. Our website has a wealth of news, ideas and information into which you can tap and there is a regular e-newsletter and a lively weekly blog to inspire you. Access our website **http://www.springboardconsultancy.com** for information about:

- Springboard Women's Development Programmes that are running
- Springboard trainers in your geographical area
- other courses
- our weekly blog with inspiring and thought provoking ideas to keep your development going
- our regular e-newsletter with news and information for anyone interested or involved in Springboard, whether you are an individual, an employer or a trainer
- how to become a Springboard trainer yourself
- how to have your staff licensed to run the Springboard Women's Development Programme in-house

We also want to hear from you! We especially love to hear stories from the people using our courses, whether you're a participant, trainer or employer, so do email us on: **office@springboardconsultancy.com**

We look forward to hearing from you.

www.springboardconsultancy.com

Other things of interest

Springboard is THE women's development programme, of which this workbook is an essential part. Tried and tested over many years, providing a powerful and life changing experience. Award winning. Available in many countries and translations.

Sprint is the ground-breaking professional development programme for undergraduate women with a special version available for post-graduate students and researchers.

Boost is the programme for people who are new to the working world. It equips them to develop their careers quickly and effectively by teaching them how to be more career savvy.

Navigator is THE development programme for men, encouraging them to examine both their home and work life to identify practical and realistic steps to fulfil their own potential.

Spring Forward is a career development programme for men and women approaching or newly appointed to a management role or as a next step after completing Springboard or Navigator.

Fresh Steps is the innovative work and personal development programme that enables people to review their professional progress, reassess their priorities and direction and set and achieve new personal and work goals.

Development Plus: this challenging and highly specialised programme, originally commissioned by the UK Home Office, has been designed to tackle the issues for women approaching the 'glass ceiling'.

Our **Trainers licensing courses** are the best in the business! Everything you need to successfully set up, promote and deliver one of our high quality programmes yourself.

About the authors

The Springboard Consultancy is a world-leading international training and development consultancy that contributes to achieving greater equality in the world by helping everyone be the best they can be and realise their full potential.

Over the 30-year heritage of delivering our successful and powerful Springboard Women's Development Programme, the Consultancy has broadened its portfolio after being approached to develop and deliver a full range of holistic development programmes, accessible to all, irrespective of age, gender or circumstance through all five life stages – both professionally and personally.

We operate globally and have a unique network of 450 licensed trainers based in over 45 counties, delivering world-class programmes with proven successful results.

The Springboard programme and this workbook were originally developed by Liz Willis and Jenny Daisley, collaborating on the research, design and delivery of a radical new programme for women in the BBC. They went on to set up the Consultancy and start training and licensing other women trainers to deliver the Springboard Women's Development Programme.

This enabled a greater impact, as more programmes could be run and the programme could be made appropriate for differing cultures, traditions and languages. They developed a reputation for their work being pragmatic, accessible and down-to-earth and this ethos continues today.

Thanks

When the first edition of Springboard was published it was a new and unprecedented idea and no one could have anticipated the global impact it now has.

The interest, enthusiasm and commitment to Springboard of many people across the globe keeps it fresh and exciting and we want to thank everyone who has contributed to this new edition of the workbook and those who have given helpful feedback and suggestions to revise and update the Springboard programme that accompanies this book.

In particular we want to thank:

The network of licensed Springboard trainers in the UK. Thanks for being the enthusiastic envoys for the programme; sharing your stories of how our materials land in the heads, hearts and hands of your participants; telling us how you personalise your delivery and giving your suggestions and feedback to improve both the workshops and this workbook.

Our Profile writers: Donna, Ruth, Sheree, Noorhan, Anne, Sally, Anjana, Sarah, Hilary, Bethan, Fiona and Vandita. Thanks for your generosity in sharing the downs as well as the ups. Your stories bring alive the issues raised in this book and demonstrate the power of taking control of your life. Thanks for allowing us a tiny peek into your amazing and inspiring lives to help others learn from your setbacks and successes.

Julie Spence, now Lord Lieutenant of Cambridgeshire. Julie has always been a champion of women's development and great supporter of the Springboard programme during her career in police services across the UK. We are delighted that she has written the Foreword to this edition.

The T4 group of trainers who train Springboard trainers. Thanks for your help with reading chapters and commenting on their development; making helpful suggestions for Profile writers; sending regular supportive communications; sharing your expert knowledge and how you interpret and work with the workshop materials.

Special thanks to the incredibly hard-working, very organised and ever cheerful team in the Springboard Consultancy virtual office for practical support, down-to-earth advice, just getting on with it and making things happen so Springboard continues to make a difference for so many women's lives.

We would like record a special thanks to Dr Sue Hewitt, one of our T4 trainers, for her enthusiastic and tireless updating of the Springboard workbook. Her passion, drive and professionalism to revise and refresh this amazing workbook that supports the Springboard programme has been incredible and we are extremely pleased that we are now able to offer a fresh, current version of the Springboard workbook. 30 years on and still as needed and effective a programme as ever! Thank you Sue!

Hundreds of thousands of women in many countries around the world have now used this book to make changes in themselves and their world, so we invite you to join them as you work through it for yourself. Thanks for trusting us to help you make a difference in your own life.

The Springboard Consultancy

NOTES

Other Titles by Hawthorn Press

Navigator
Work and Personal Development for Men
James Traeger, Jenny Daisley, Liz Willis

This 4th edition of the *Navigator* workbook is an integral part of the Navigator Development Programme for Men. It is for all men at work or seeking work: for men on their own, men in relationships and men as fathers. Packed with ideas and practical exercises to assess yourself, identify where you want to go in life, it equips you with the positive attitude and many of the skills needed to get you there. Navigator is the tried, tested and successful parallel programme to the award-winning Springboard Women's Development Programme.

416pp; 246 × 189mm; pb; 978-1-912480-06-7

The Parenting Toolkit
Simple steps to happy & confident children
Caroline Penney

This book is a unique and valuable resource for parents and guardians who wish to give their children the best start in life. The author has drawn on her years of experience facilitating parenting groups and working as a family therapist to present these techniques clearly, illustrated by a wealth of real-life examples. She offers simple skills for developing healthier relationships with children of all ages. She also has advice on how to manage parents'/guardians' own stress and ensure they are getting the self-care that they need.

176pp; 250 × 200mm; pb; 978-1-91248011-1

Form Drawing and Colouring
For Fun, Healing and Wellbeing
Angela Lord

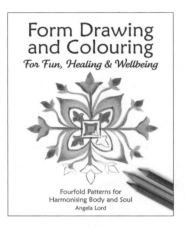

Creative form drawing is a fascinating and meaningful artistic activity for health and wellbeing. *Form Drawing and Colouring: for Fun, Healing and Wellbeing* offers space for personal creativity, with stunning colourful forms to stimulate originality. Engaging the right side of the brain through the flow of colour, form and movement, it aims be both calming and enlivening, and is a valuable aid to harmonising body and soul.

96pp; 246 × 189mm; pb; 978-1-907359-78-1

Making The Children's Year
Marije Rowling

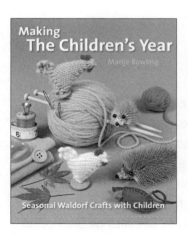

Drawing on the creative ethos of Steiner Waldorf education, this is a full-colour second edition of *The Children's Year,* which has been a much-loved favourite for over thirty years. From beginners to experienced crafters, this book is packed with all kinds of crafts, from papercrafting to building dens, and brings the seasons into the home. A perfect gift for parents and adults seeking to make toys that will inspire children and provide an alternative to throwaway culture.

240pp; 250 x 200mm; pb; 978-1-907359-69-9

Making Simple Needle Felts

Steffi Stern

Steffi Stern brings her inimitable energy and enthusiasm to her second book, intended as a back-to-basics guide to making needle-felted objects. All the projects in the book are achievable for a beginner. Some aimed at little fingers (no needles involved) and beginners, and some are aimed at those with more experience. The book is organised by season; it brims with all kinds of treasures, such as pumpkins, gnomes, strawberries, baubles, birds, bees, snails, flowers, the Nativity, mice, and mermaids. Steffi's advice is to have a go!

160pp; 250 x 200mm; pb; 978-1-907359-97-2

The Natural Storyteller

Wildlife Tales for Telling

Georgiana Keable

In these pages you will find over fifty nature stories, chosen to bring both teller and listener closer to their environment. These culturally diverse stories that have stood the test of time will engage young readers, and encourage them to become natural storytellers. The stories are accompanied by tips on telling, story maps, and practical activities.

272pp; 228 x 186mm; pb; 978-1-907359-80-4

An A-Z Collection of Behaviour Tales

From Angry Ant to Zestless Zebra

Susan Perrow

Illustrated by Allmut ffrench

Telling the right story at the right time can help children face challenges and change behaviour. All 42 stories begin with an undesirable or out-of-balance situation and, through the use of metaphor and an imaginative story journey, lead to a more desirable resolution. The stories, some humorous, some serious, are especially relevant for children aged three to nine years. They are for telling and adapting: turn them into home-made picture books or puppet shows, or even create new tales from them.

144pp; 234 x 156mm; pb; 978-1-907359-86-6

Free, Equal and Mutual

Rebalancing Society for the Common Good

Edited by Martin Large and Steve Briault

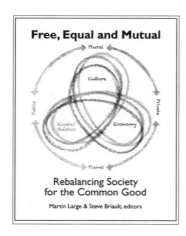

Currently, our market-dominated society is in meltdown and people feel afraid for their jobs, families and identity. *Free, Equal and Mutual* is a centenary anthology that draws on Rudolf Steiner's vision for a free, equal and mutual society, a threefold commonwealth. 20 cutting edge articles by 13 contributors offer a timely alternative for rebalancing society.

234 x 156mm; 260pp; pb; 978-1-907359-94-1

Ordering books

If you have difficulties ordering Hawthorn Press books from a bookshop, you can order direct from our website **www.hawthornpress.com**, or from our UK distributor:

BookSource
50 Cambuslang Road, Glasgow, G32 8NB
Tel: (0845) 370 0063
E-mail: orders@booksource.net

Details of our overseas distributors can be found on our website.
www.hawthornpress.com

HAWTHORN PRESS